# CONTRACTOR BUSINESS NEXT LEVEL

## TENNESSEE

# 1 CONTRACTOR CLUB

## The #1 Contractor Service Provider

Tennessee's #1 contracting school for over 15 years now offers expanded contractor services.

---

### 1 EXAM PREP
AMERICA'S #1 CONTRACTOR SCHOOL

## Contractor Exam Prep

- ⊘ Live Virtual Classes
- ⊘ Online Courses & Tutoring
- ⊘ Exam Book Rental
- ⊘ Application Assistance

USE CODE **CLUB24**
**FOR 10% OFF!**

---

### 1 INSURANCE SOLUTIONS
AMERICA'S #1 CONTRACTOR INSURANCE

## Contractor Insurance

- ⊘ General Liability Insurance
- ⊘ Builder's Risk Insurance
- ⊘ Workers' Compensation.
- ⊘ Life & Health Insurance

Scan Now
**Get a Free Quote!**

---

### 1 CONTRACTOR SOLUTIONS
AMERICA'S #1 CONTRACTOR SERVICES PROVIDER

## Contractor Permits

- ⊘ Permit Expediters
- ⊘ General Trade Permits
- ⊘ License Registration
- ⊘ NOC Recording

USE CODE **PERMIT24**
**50% OFF Your First Permit!**

---

1ExamPrep.com
**(877) 775-9400**

1InsuranceSolutions.com
**(877) 700-0243**

1ContractorSolutions.com
**(877) 702-5377**

Author: One Exam Prep (1-877-804-3959)
www.1examprep.com

AGENCY

PRIVACY.FLOWCODE.COM

**VISIT US HERE FOR EXCLUSIVE OFFERS**

# Unleashing the Power Of Digital Marketing For Your Contractor Business

- Company Branding
- Contractor Website
- Social Media Templates
- 1-on-1 Marketing Consultations
- Google Search Optimazation

## WWW.154AGENCY.COM

# TABLE OF CONTENTS

---

## Testing Company Info

**Below is the testing company information you will need concerning your exam.**

PSI has examination centers in many other regions across the United States. You may take the written examination at any of these locations by filling out, and faxing the Special Arrangement Form found at the end of this bulletin.

For all state specific information please visit - PSI Exam License Page

1. Select Your State Jurisdiction - TN
2. Select Account - Your Appropriate License Category
3. Select Your License Classification

**All questions and requests for information about examinations should be directed to PSI.**

**PSI Licensure:Certification**
3210 E Tropicana
Las Vegas, NV 89121
(800) 733-9267 • Fax (702) 932-2666
www.psiexams.com

**If you are having problems opening the pdf links to practice tests, highlights & tabs, and answers. You may have to update your adobe reader.**

# Examination Outline

There are 40 questions in this examination. You will need to answer 29 correctly to pass. You are allowed 135 minutes to complete this examination. This examination is OPEN book.

## Exam Specs

| | |
|---|---|
| Total Questions | 40 |
| Time Limit: | 135 Mins |

## Content Outline

| Subject Area | # of Questions |
|---|---|
| General Knowlege and Math | 5 |
| General Requirements (not including Gas) - Admin., Structural, Backflow, Materials, & Supports, Joints & Connections, Storm Drains, Testing | 4 |
| Water Supply and Dist. | 4 |
| Fixture, including Water Heaters | 2 |
| Drain, Waste, and Vent Systems, including Indirect and Special Waste | 10 |
| Traps, Cleanouts, and Interceptors | 2 |
| Isometric Analysis | 7 |
| Gas Appliances and Piping | 4 |
| OSHA Safety | 2 |

**Total Questions: 40**

## SECURITY PROCEDURES

The Plumbing Contractor examinations are OPEN book. Candidates may bring reference books listed in this bulletin. Reference books may be highlighted, underlined, and/or indexed. They must be otherwise unmarked (not written in) and may not contain additional papers (loose or attached). **Proctors will thoroughly inspect all books before and after your examination.**

Reference books may not have removable tabs. The list below is a guide only, and does not guarantee that you will be able to use them. However if they are applied correctly, these tabs will stick onto pages and will tear the page if you try to remove them. This is only a sample list

**NO MATTER WHAT IS ON THE TAB PACKAGE, IF THE PSI PROCTOR IS ABLE TO REMOVE THE TABS WITHOUT RIPPING THE PAGE, YOU WILL NEED TO REMOVE THE TABS BEFORE YOU TAKE THE EXAM. DO NOT USE THE TABS THAT HAVE PAPER INSERTS. THE PAPER INSERTS WILL BE REMOVED.**

## Acceptable Tabs

- Avery Swift Tabs Self-Adhesive Permanent Plastic Tabs
- Redi-Tag Self-Stick Permanent Adhesive Index Tabs

## Unacceptable Tabs

- Post-It Index Flags
- Post-It Flags

The reference materials listed below were used to prepare the questions for this examination. The examination may also contain questions based on trade knowledge or general industry practices. Except for Code books, you can base your answers on later editions of references as they become available. For Code questions, the examinations will be based only on the edition of the Code book that is listed. Candidates may use a silent, non-printing, non-programmable calculator in the examination center. Candidates will also be provided with a magnifying glass upon request. The following reference materials are allowed in the examination center:

## Approved References

1. International Plumbing Code, 2012
2. International Fuel Gas Code, 2012
3. Mathematics for Plumbers and Pipefitters, 8th Edition, 2013
4. Code of Federal Regulations - 29 CFR Part 1926 (OSHA)

# STRATEGY FOR TEST TAKING

The preparation for an exam starts at the beginning of the course. It is essential to have the subject's program, become aware of the program, know it, review the books and support materials, and attend classes or tutoring sessions. The greater the time invested in preparing for your exam,the more likely you will pass it the first time around. The exam is just the first goal of a long career.

## Prepare Mentally and Physically

Preparing for the exams depends, to a large extent, on the way you study. But other factors directly influence your academic performance, such as diet and exercise. Although the idea is to maintain a healthy and balanced diet throughout the year and exercise regularly, it is even more essential when preparing for your exams.

It is about eating breakfast that gives us the energy to face the day and supply the brain with enough glucose to get the most out of our study hours. Hydrating correctly for the day with water, dividing meals into five or six, and not overdoing it with caffeine will enhance our ability to pay attention and improve memory.

**The same thing happens with exercise:** Exercising will help us remove stress, rest better, and wake up feeling refreshed and more alert. Regular exercise also improves learning on two levels: it boosts cognitive function and memory retention. The more oxygenated nutrients the brain gets, the better it can perform, especially during exams.

**Study planning:** The first step to successfully passing the exams is planning well. This involves studying the subjects or content areas that will be on the exam daily. As the day of the exam approaches, we will only have to do an in-depth review of the entire exam scope to reach the exam date with all the suitably prepared subjects.

**Reading:** It is the general way to get in touch with a topic. When reading the scope of the exam, we must identify different phases for reading comprehension. First, we must understand the text's ideas and then expose our doubts or convey to the instructor what we have not understood. After examining what we read, we will achieve a broad vision of the whole, and it will only be enough for us to look for the general ideas.

**Highlighting the text:** Highlighting will help us focus on the relevant information in the text, and later, will help us structure and organize for the actual exam. We will avoid overloading the text excessively with highlights, not to hinder the ability to find the right answers during the exam. Note: Most testing companies allow the references for open book exams to be highlighted and tabbed with permanently affixed tabs. Be sure to check with your State or Local Jurisdiction regarding your exam.

**Organizational techniques:** Organizing the study material is key to understanding the concepts that we have previously highlighted in the text. These techniques will help us clarify the subject's structure, order the ideas hierarchically, and shorten the text's length to facilitate review and active study.

**Study sheets:** Using study cards or flashcards may sound like a very old-fashioned technique, but it is quite an effective learning method for assimilating specific data. It is about making a 'mini summary' of an entire topic, which allows you to save a lot when creating them, and they are straightforward to consult.

**Take Practice Tests:** The practice tests are an excellent way to review before an exam; in addition to that, with these, you can check what you are failing and focus efforts where necessary. It is, without a doubt, one of the best study strategies!

## How Can You Improve Your Exam Preparation?

**Make sure:**

- Study daily to make sure you understand the subject.
- Study each subject listed on the exam scope: highlight, make outlines, and summaries.
- When a topic is well learned, it is not easily forgotten. In studying the following topics, you will have to rely on the previous ones, serving as a review and consolidation.

- When the exam approaches, we have to review to anchor them more in memory.

## How Can You Improve Taking the Exam?

- Losing the nerve before the exam: "nerves are useless and they are in the way of everything."
- Try to relax. Practice relaxation techniques.
- Do not try to check if you remember all the exam subjects; before the exam, your mind is in tension, you can no longer reinforce your memory, so concentrate on what you will do.
- Being physically and mentally fit: You must sleep well and get enough rest before the exam.
- Do not leave everything for the last moment; if you do, you give the memory time to settle the information it receives. The memory needs rest, and your memory will be more clear if there is order.

# How Fully Understand the Exam Questions?

- Leave the nerves at home.
- Take your time to read the questions well. Read them all. Sometimes there may be more than one referring to the same topic, and you will have to decide the focus and content for each one.
- Before answering each particular question, read it several times until you make sure you understand it. Look for the keyword that tells you what to do: explain, demonstrate, define, calculate, find. If your exam is open book, look for keywords that will indicate which book to find the answer in — Practice Comprehensive Reading.
- After answering, reread the question and answers and double-check your selection.

# How to Organize the Time You Have During the Exam?

- It is necessary to know each question's value since the same amount of time may not be devoted to each question or subject.
- Quick distribution of time is made. We must allow time for review.
- It would be best to start with the questions that you are familiar with and know the answers quickly. The best way to answer is by making, in the beginning, an outline that guides us during the exam.
- When there is no time to answer a question, don't leave the question not answered. It will be an automatic wrong answer rather than taking a 1 out of 4 chance of getting the answer correct.

# How to Review and Correct the Exam?

- Before submitting the exam, you should review:

**The content:** Make sure that you have answered all the questions.

**The form:**

It is more than obvious to say that to pass any exam depends a lot on how you study, the time you dedicate, and the information retention capacity you have.

- However, it also requires taking into account many other factors, so the best we can do is use effective study techniques to help you pass that stressful exam.
- It is expected that as the exam approaches, nerves can begin to take over due to the lack of constant study. That is why it is essential to discover an ideal technique that will lead you to achieve success and pass.

# Preparation to Examinations

As we previously mentioned, preparation for your exam starts at the beginning of the course. It is essential to have the subject's program, become aware of the program, know it, review the books and support materials, and attend classes or tutoring sessions. The more time invested in preparing for your exam, the more likely you will pass it the first time.

It is also essential to keep motivation high when studying and have a learning strategy for each subject. Above all, you should not fear exploring different study methods.

## Conclusively, We Can Develop the Following Strategies

**Method One:**

You should not "jump" on the exam task immediately after you received it. It would also be best if you didn't go through the questions one at a time in their original order.

Observe the following procedure:

Read the directions very carefully. The exam instructions often contain valuable data. Always examine all guidelines carefully to make sure you understand what's being requested.

Take a deep breath, and then slowly scan your eyes throughout the exam to familiarize yourself with all the questions.

In the process, answer the questions to which you know the correct answer.

Tackle more difficult tasks, but don't spend too much time on them. Leave the most difficult questions for the end.

Your task is to give as many correct answers to questions that you are sure of. Scientists have proven that when you skim through the entire test, unresolved questions are already "looming" in your head even before seriously tackling its solution. This is very useful for a variety of reasons.

First, you subconsciously start thinking about a solution to the most challenging test questions.

Secondly, tests often come across questions containing hints and sometimes even a complete answer to other test questions.

In any case, before proceeding with the solution of exam tasks, first, review the questions and give answers where you can do it. Then start to puzzle over more complicated tasks.

**Method Two:**

Read each test question at least twice.

This is a handy tip because trick questions are widespread in tests. When we are in the exam, we want to solve the tasks as quickly as possible, as there is not enough time. Therefore, many students make a widespread mistake because they glimpse a question and immediately start sorting out the answers.

The fact is that test developers try to outwit the exam takers and dilute the standard tasks with tricky questions. Let's take a look at some of them:

In tests, you can often come across the following question: Which of the following does not contain "a," "b," or "c"? If you read the task inattentively, it is quite possible to quickly skip the "not" particle and give a wrong answer.

Other questions may contain several correct answers, and your task involves choosing the most correct one.

Summing up, you should not lose your vigilance since inattention often leads to mistakes. So, do not be lazy and reread the questions at least twice.

**Method Three:**

Double-check the answers right away, rather than postpone checking until the end.

The fact is that once you have answered the question, the information is still very fresh in your head. Therefore, by quickly checking your answers, you will significantly reduce the chances of accidentally missing one silly mistake. On the other hand, you will increase your chances of receiving a passing exam score.

However, this does not mean that you should not recheck your answers after solving all the tests. On the contrary, try to always leave some time for final checking. By adding this technique to your arsenal, you can undoubtedly increase the chance of getting a decent grade.

**Method Four (for closed book exams):**

If you come across a question, the answer to which you do not remember, or you feel that it literally "spins on the tongue" but does not come to mind, try to mentally transfer yourself to the place where you first heard about it.

**There are 24 hours in a day. If 8 of them are spent sleeping, that gives you 16 hours to get some efficient and productive study done, right?**

**It seems simple enough. There are plenty of hours in a day, so why is it so hard to use this time effectively, especially around exam time?**

We've found that managing their time effectively is one of the things that students struggle the most with around exam time. However, time management is also one of the things that schools never teach – how frustrating?!

In the weeks leading up to study leave, every teacher you have for every class you go to seems to pile on the work: Mrs Gibb from English class tells you that you have to prepare 3 practice essays for both your visual and written texts, your Geography teacher Miss Wood expects you to do every past exam paper for the last three years before the exam, Mr West your Maths teacher says that you have to finish all of the questions in that darned AME textbook if you want to do well on the exam.

But they expect you to do all of this without giving you any time management tips. Mrs Gibb, Miss Wood and Mr West all fail to tell you how it's humanly possible to complete all of this work without collapsing when you walk into the exam hall.

**That's where we come in!**

**Read on for the time management tips that your teachers never gave you!**

1. Focus on what you have to study – not what you don't.

It seems obvious, but think of all the times you've sat down to study and you've ended up spending 2 hours studying the concepts you already know like the back of your hand.

It's easier to study the subjects you like. Studying the concepts that you're already confident in is a lot less challenging than studying the concepts that you find the most difficult, as your brain will have to work less to learn this information.

Studying what you already know is a bad time management strategy because you'll leave all the important stuff to the last minute meaning you won't have the time to cover these concepts in depth.

The trouble with this tip is that it's often hard to decipher what you know and what you don't.

To figure out what you concepts you already know, and what concepts you still need to learn, complete a subject audit. A subject audit involves breaking down a particular subject into several points or sections and then analysing how well you know each of these points. You should spend most of your time studying those concepts that you have rated the most difficult. Find our study audit outline form here.

**The key for effective time management is to review the easier material, but allow enough time to cover the harder concepts in depth so you're not left to study all of the most difficult concepts the night before the exam.**

## 2. Work in sprints.

You may think that to have good time management skills you have to spend all of your time studying. However this is a misconception that many students hold.

Think of studying for exams like training for a marathon.

On your first day of training, you wouldn't go out and run 42kms. You would burn-out quickly due to a lack of prior training, and you would probably be put off running for a long time. This would not be a good way to manage your time. The better route to success would be to slowly work up to running the 42kms by running a bit further every day.

**This simple idea of training in short bursts has been proven effective in all areas of human performance.** You don't have to be a marathon runner to use this strategy!

**When studying, you should start out small by studying in short, focused 'sprints' followed by brief breaks.** Start by studying in 15 minute bursts followed by one 10 minute break. Over time, slowly increase the length of time you're studying (and breaking) for.

This strategy is effective because studying for short bursts promotes more intense focus, and will give your brain the time to process and consolidate information as opposed to studying for long periods of time which is not effective and may increase your chances of burnout.

**Don't think of effective time management as studying for three hours straight with no breaks, think of effective time management as using your time wisely and in ways that will best promote retention of information.**

Follow these steps to practice effective time management and become an expert studier (or marathon runner!) in no time:

1. **Set a timer for 15 minutes.**
2. **Put in some solid study until the timer goes off, making sure you're spending every minute working with no distractions.**
3. **Have a ten-minute break to check your phone, walk around, stretch, get outside etc.**
4. **Rinse and repeat.**
5. **Increase the amount of time you're studying for as you begin to feel more comfortable studying for extended lengths of time.**

## 3. Make a study system.

I'm sure you've been lectured by every teacher you've ever had to "make a study plan!!!" Study plans are effective for your time management, however they're sometimes hard to stick to.

Here at StudyTime, we find that the 'study system' is an effective strategy for really getting to the root of what you're studying. A study system is easier to stick to, and therefore fosters better time management skills, because it breaks tasks down into small chunks.

A study system is basically a simple list of steps that you can make to outline the steps you're going to take when you study. The list should start simple (4-5 things), but over time it should become more complex as you add steps to it.

**Just like a workout plan at the gym or for sport, it will give you a clear direction of what action to take, making study much more efficient.**

Over time, you can experiment with new study methods, and add them in to optimise the system.

Below is an example study formula that you could use when studying:

1. **Download the "Achievement Standard" from the NCEA website**
2. **Turn this into a checklist for what you already know and what you need to know**
3. **Break the checklist into main themes using a mind map**
4. **For each theme, make a summary sheet**
5. **After that, break down the key points of each summary and put these onto flash cards**
6. **Read through your notes and ensure you understand them, and then hit the flash cards**
7. **Test yourself on all of them first, then make two piles, one that's wrong and one that's right. Then redo the wrong pile again**
8. **Get someone else to test you**
9. **Practice exam papers – test yourself using exam papers from the past 2-3 years and time yourself**
10. **Work through the answers**
11. **Write a sheet of all tips/tricks i.e. things you got wrong in the practice exam papers**
12. **Redo exam paper and make model answers**
13. **Adjust flashcards if necessary i.e. make new ones based on the exam papers**
14. **Re-test all your flashcards**

Creating a study system will keep you on track and it will allow you to effectively plan out your time while studying.

## 4. Practice distributed learning.

Imagine your Maths teacher gave you seven equations to do for homework. How would you answer these questions? Would you do one question per day for seven days, or would you do all seven questions in one day?

You may think that it would be a better time management strategy to do all seven questions at once and get them over and done with. However, this is an ineffective way to manage your time.

**The brain works better when it has time to process information.** Neuroscience has shown that your brain needs time to consolidate information that has been newly learned, in order to form strong links between neurons and thus strong memories.

If the learning is done in one big chunk, you'll just forget it after three days. However, if you review it a day after, then you'll retain it for seven days.

**When making a study schedule, you should space out when you study for each subject.** For example, don't spend one day studying English, then the next day studying Maths, then the next day studying Biology. Instead, you should alternate studying for these subjects throughout the day. Do one hour of Maths, then one hour of English study, then one hour of Biology, and so on.

This is a much better way to manage your time, because the more often you review a concept, the more solidified it will be in your mind. This is because there will be more time to consolidate this into your memory. Also, taking breaks between reviewing certain concepts will give your brain time to process the information.

**Try it out!**

# 1 Exam Prep
# International Fuel Gas Code 2012
# Tabs and Highlights

These 1 Exam Prep Tabs are based on the *International Fuel GasCode-Building-2012 Edition.*

Each Tabs sheet has five rows of tabs. Start with the first tab at the first row at the top of the page, and proceed down that row placing the tabs at the locations listed below. Place each tab in your book setting it down one notch until you get to the bottom of the page, and then start back at the top again. After you have completed tabbing your book (the last tab is usually the glossary, appendix, or index), then you may start highlighting your book.

<u>Special note to our Students</u>: If you are a 1 Exam Prep student, here is how to really get the most from these 1 Exam Prep Tabs. Follow the above instructions, but before placing the tab, find the tab's topic in the outline of your appropriate module. Now locate and highlight several items listed in the outline just before and just after the topic. See how the topic fits in the outline and how it relates as a concept to the broader concept spelled out in the outline. If you take a few minutes to do this, when you take the test, key words in the test questions will remind you of where the information is in the manual!

*This concludes the tabs for this book. Please continue with the highlights on the following page.*

| | |
|---|---|
|

| Section # | Highlight |
|---|---|
| 403.6.3 | **Regulator vent piping.** Plastic pipe and…be installed indoors. |
| 403.9.2 | **Number of threads.** Field threading of…with Table 403.9.2 |
| Table 403.9.2 | **Specifications for Threading Metallic Pipe**<br>- Left column – Iron Pipe Size<br>- Middle column – Approx. Length of Threaded Portion<br>- Right column – Approx. Number of Threads to be cut |
| 403.10.1 | **Pipe joints.** Pipe joints shal…0.05-percent phosphorus.' |
| 404 | **Piping System Installation** |
| 404.6 | **Underground penetrations prohibited**: Gas piping shall not penetrate building foundation walls … the pipe and the wall shall be sealed. |
| 404.7 | **Protection against physical damage.** Protective steel shield…joist or rafter. |
| 404.9 | **Above-ground outdoor piping.** All piping installed…the roof surface. |
| 404.12 | **Minimum burial depth.** Underground piping systems….in Section 404.12.1 |
| 404.16 | **Location of outlets.** The unthreaded portion…2 inches (51 mm). |
| 404.17.1 | **Limitations**<br><br>**Exceptions:**<br>(See #3 Only) |
| 405 | **Piping Bends and Changes in Direction** |
| 405.2 | **Metallic pipe:** 4. Pipe shall not be bent through an arc of more than 90 degrees. |
| 406 | **Inspection, Testing and Purging** |
| 406.2 | **Test medium:** The test medium shall be air, … Oxygen shall not be used. |
| 406.4.1 | **Test pressure.** The test pressure…than 3 psig. |
| 406.4.2 | **Test duration.** The duration of…exceed 24 hours. |
| 408 | **Drips and Sloped Piping** |
| 408.4 | **Sediment trap:** Where sediment trap is not incorporated as part of the appliance … to the inlet of the appliance as practical. |
| 410 | **Flow Control** |
| 410.2 | **MP Regulators**: Mp pressure regulators shall comply with the following: 6. A tee fitting with one opening capped … pressure measuring instrument. |

| Section # | Highlight |
|---|---|
| 411 | **Appliance Manufactured Home Connections** |
| 411.1.3.1 | **Maximum length:** Connectors shall have an overall length not to exceed 6 feet. |
| 411.1.6 | **Unions.** A union fitting…of the appliance. |
| 413.8 | **Emergency shutdown control.** An emergency shutdown…the compressor area. |
| 413.9.2.5 | **Vent tube.** The vent tube…above grade level. |
| Table 415.1 | **Supporting of Piping:**<br>- 1st Column: Pipe Size<br>- 2nd Column: Spacing of supports<br>- 3rd Column: Tubing size<br>- 4th Column: Spacing of Supports |
| 501 | **General** |
| 501.9 | **Chimney entrance:** Connectors shall connect to a masonry chimney … lowest portion of the interior of the chimney flue. |
| 501.12 | **Residential and low-heat appliances flue lining systems.** |
| 501.15.3 | **Cleanout.** Masonry chimney flues…chimney inlet opening. |
| 502 | **Vents** |
| 502.4 | **Insulation shield.** Where vents pass…the insulation material. |
| 502.7 | **Protection against physical damage.** Protective steel shield…joist or rafter. |
| 503 | **Venting or Appliances** |
| 503.3.3 | **Mechanical draft systems.** Mechanical draft systems shall comply with the following: (See #6 Only) |
| Table 503.4 | **Type of Venting System To Be Used**<br>- Left Column: Appliances<br>- Right Column: Type of Venting System |
| 503.3.5 | **Air ducts and furnace plenumns**: Venting systems shall not extend into … or furnace plenum. |
| 503.5.4 | **Chimney termination** |
| 503.6.5 | **Minimum height.** A Type B or….or flue collar. |
| 503.7.5 | **Roof penetrations** |

# 1 Exam Prep
# International Plumbing Code, 2012
# Tabs and Highlights

These 1 Exam Prep Tabs are based on the *Florida Plumbing Code, 2012*.

Each 1 Exam Prep tabs sheet has five rows of tabs. Start with the first tab at the first row at the top of the page; proceed down that row placing the tabs at the locations listed below. Place each tab in your book setting it down one notch until you get to the last tab (usually the index or glossary). Then start with the highlights.

| **1 Exam Prep Tab** | **Section/Page #** |
| --- | --- |
| Table of Contents | Pg. xiii |
| Scope and Admin | 100 |
| Permits | 106 |
| Inspections & Testing | 107 |
| Means of Appeal | 109 |
| Definitions | 202 |
| General Regulations | 300 |
| Piping Support | 308 |
| Fixtures, Faucets, & Fittings | 400 |
| Minimum Plumbing Facilities | 403 |
| Water Heaters | 500 |
| Water Supply & Distribution | 600 |
| Materials, Joints & Connections | 605 |
| Protection of Potable Water Supply | 608 |
| Sanitary Drainage | 700 |
| Joints | 705 |
| Cleanouts | 708 |

*\*\*\*This concludes the tabs for this book. Please continue with the highlights on the following page.\*\*\**

| Section # | Highlight |
|-----------|-----------|
| 202 | **General Definitions**<br>- Backflow<br>- Back pressure, low head<br>- Backflow connection<br>- Backsiphonage<br>- Bedpan steamer or boiler<br>- Developed length<br>- Offset<br>- Potable water |
| 305 | **Protection of Pipes and Plumbing System Components** |
| 306 | **Trenching, Excavation and Backfill** |
| 307 | **Structural Safety** |
| 307.5 | **Trench location:** Trenches installed parallel to footings shall not extend below the 45-degree bearing plane of the footing or wall. |
| 308 | **Piping Support** |
| 308.5 | **Interval of support**: Pipe shall be supported in accordance with Table 308.5. |
| Table 308.5 | **Hanger Spacing** |
| 308.8 | **Expansion joint fittings** |
| 310 | **Washroom and Toilet Room Requirements** |
| 310.1 | **Light and Ventilation:** Washrooms and toilet rooms shall be illuminated and ventilated in accordance with the Florida Building Code, Building and the Florida Building Code, Mechanical. |
| 312 | **Tests and Inspections** |
| 312.2 | **Drainage and vent water test:** If the system is tested in sections, each opening shall be tightly plugged except the highest openings … This pressure shall be held for not less than 15 minutes. |
| 312.6 | **Gravity sewer test:** Gravity sewer tests shall consist of plugging the end of the building sewer at the point of connection … with not less than a 10-foot head of water and maintaining such pressure for 15 minutes. |
| 312.7 | **Forced sewer test:** Forced sewer tests shall consist of plugging the end of the building sewer at the point of connection with the public sewer and applying a pressure of 5 psi greater than the pump rating, and maintaining such pressure for 15 minutes. |

| Section # | Highlight |
|---|---|
| **402** | **Fixture Materials** |
| 402.3 | **Sheet copper**: Sheet copper for general applications shall conform to ASTM B 152 and shall not weigh less than 12 ounces per square foot. |
| **403** | **Minimum Plumbing Facilities** |
| 403.1 | **Minimum number of fixtures:** Plumbing fixtures shall be provided for the type of occupancy and in the minimum number shown in Table 403.1. |
| Table 403.1 | **Minimum Number of Required Plumbing Fixtures** |
| 403.3.3 | **Location of toilet facilities in occupancies other than covered malls:** shall be located not more than one story above … shall not exceed a distance of 500 feet. |
| **405** | **Installation of Fixtures** |
| 405.3.1 | **Water closets, urinals, lavatories and bidets:** A water closet, urinal, lavatory or bidet shall not be set closer than 15 inches from its center to any side wall … Water closet compartments shall be less than 30 inches in width and not less than 60 inches in depth for floor-mounted water closets and not less than 30 inches in width and 56 inches in depth for wall hung water closets. |
| 405.8 | **Slip joint connections:** Fixtures with concealed slip-joint connections shall be provided with an access panel or utility space not less than 12-inches in its smallest dimension or other approved arrangement so as to provide access to the slip joint connections for inspection and repair. |
| **409** | **Dishwashing Machines** |
| 409.1 | **Approval**: Commercial dishwashing machines shall conform to ASSE 1004 and NSF 3. |
| **411** | **Emergency Showers and Eyewash Stations** |
| 411.2 | **Waste connection:** Waste connections shall not be required for emergency showers and eyewash stations. |
| **412** | **Floor and Trench Drains** |
| 412.3 | **Size of floor drains:** Floor drains shall have a drain outlet not less than 2 inches in diameter. |
| **413** | **Food Waste Grinder Units** |
| 413.3 | **Commercial food waste grinder waste outlets:** Commercial food waste grinders shall be connected to a drain not less than 1 ½ inches in diameter. |

| **Section #** | **Highlight** |
|---|---|

**413.4**     **Water supply required:** All food waste grinders shall be provided with a supply of cold water. The water supply shall be protected against backflow by an air gap or backflow preventer in accordance with Section 608.

**417**     **Showers**

**417.4.1**     **Wall area:** The wall area above built-in tubs with installed shower heads and in shower compartments shall be constructed of smooth … to a height not less than 6 feet above the room floor level, and not less than 70 inches where measured from the compartment floor at the drain.

**417.5.2.1**     **PVC sheets:** Plasticized polyvinyl chloride (PVC) sheets shall meet the requirements of ASTM D 4551. Sheets can be joined in accordance with the Manufacturer's instructions.

**417.5.2.2**     **Chlorinated polyethylene (CPE) sheets:** Nonplasticized chlorinated polyethylene sheet shall meet the requirements of ASTM D 4068. The liner shall be joined in accordance with the manufacturer's installation instructions.

**419**     **Urinals**

**419.2**     **Substitution for water closets:** In each bathroom or toilet room, urinals shall not be substituted for more than 67 percent of the required water closets in assembly and educational occupancies.

**421**     **Whirlpool Bathtubs**

**421.3**     **Drain:** The pump drain and circulation piping shall be sloped to drain the water in the volute and the circulation piping when the whirlpool bathtub is empty.

**425**     **Flushing Devices for Water Closets and Urinals**

**425.1.1**     **Separate for each fixture:** A flushing device shall not serve more than one fixture.

**501.2**     **Water heater as space heater:** Where a combination potable water heating and space heating system requires water for space heating at temperatures higher than 140 F … the potable hot water distribution system of 140 F or less.

**502**     **Installation**

**502.1.1**     **Elevation and protection:** Elevation of water heater ignition sources and mechanical damage protection requirements for water heaters, shall be in accordance with the International Building Code, Mechanical and the International Building Code, Fuel Gas.

**502.5**     **Clearances for maintenance and replacement:** A level working space not less than 30 inches in length and 30 inches in width shall be provided in front of the control side to service and appliance.

| Section # | Highlight |
|---|---|
| **503** | **Connections** |
| 503.1 | **Cold water line valve:** The cold water branch line from the main water supply line to each hot water storage tank or water heater shall be provided with a valve, located near the equipment and serving only the hot water storage tank or water heater. |
| **504** | **Safety Devices** |
| 504.4 | **Relief valve:** Storage water heaters operating above atmospheric pressure shall be provided with an approved, self-closing pressure relief valve and temperature relief valve or combination thereof. |
| 504.7 | **Required pan:** Where a storage tank-type water heater or a hot water storage tank is installed in a location … galvanized steel pan having a material thickness of not less than 0.0236 inch (No. 24 gage), or other pans approved for such use. |
| 504.7.1 | **Pan size and drain:** The pan shall be not less than 1 ½ inches in depth and shall be of sufficient size … having a diameter of not less than ¾ inch. Piping for safety pan drains shall be of those materials listed in Table 605.4. |
| 504.7.2 | **Pan drain termination:** The pan drain shall extend full-size and terminate over a suitably located … and terminate not less than 6 inches and not more than 24 inches above the adjacent ground surface. |
| **505** | **Insulation** |
| 505.1 | **Unfired vessel insulation:** Unfired hot water storage tanks shall be insulated to R-12.5. |
| **603** | **Water Service** |
| 603.1 | **Size of water service pipe:** The water service pipe shall be not less than ¾ inch in diameter. |
| 603.2 | **Separation of water service and building sewer:** Water service pipe and the building sewer shall be separated by not less than 5 feet of undisturbed or compacted earth. |
| | **Exceptions:** 1 -3. |
| **604** | **Design of Building Water Distribution System** |
| 604.3 | **Water distribution system design criteria:** The water distribution system shall be designed, and pipe sizes shall be selected such that under conditions of peak demand, the capacities at the fixture supply pipe outlets shall not be less than shown in Table 604.3. |
| Table 604.3 | **Water Distribution System Design Criteria Required Capacity at Fixture Supply Pipe Outlets** |

| Section # | Highlight |
|---|---|
| 604.5 | **Size and fixture supply:** The minimum size of a fixture supply pipe shall be shown in Table 604.5. |
| 604.7 | **Inadequate water pressure:** Wherever water pressure from the street main or other source of supply is insufficient to provide flow pressures at fixture outlets as required under table 604.3, a water pressure booster system conforming to Section 606.5 shall be installed on the building water supply system. |
| Table 604.5 | **Minimum Sizes of Fixture Water Supply Pipes** |
| 605 | **Materials, Joints and Connections** |
| 605.3 | **Water service pipe:** water service pipe or tubing, installed underground and outside the structure, shall have a working pressure rating of not less than 160 psi at 73.4 F. |
| 605.4 | **Water distribution pipe:** water distribution pipe shall conform to NSF 61 and shall conform to one of the standards listed in Table 605.4. Hot water distribution pipe and tubing shall have a pressure rating of not less than 100 psi at 180 F. |
| Table 605.4 | **Water Distribution Pipe** |
| 605.9 | **Prohibited joints and connections:** The following types of joints and connections shall be prohibited: 1-4. |
| 606 | **Installation of the Building Water Distribution System** |
| 606.5.1 | **Water pressure booster system required:** Where the water pressure in the public water main or individual water supply system is insufficient ... pressure booster pump installed in accordance with Section 606.5.5. |
| 606.5.6 | **Potable water inlet control and location:** Potable water inlets to gravity tanks shall be controlled by a fill valve ... The inlet shall be terminated so as to provide an air gap not less than 4 inches above the overflow. |
| 608 | **Protection of Potable Water Supply** |
| 608.8 | **Identification of non-potable water:** All non-potable water outlets such as hose connections ... The letters of the words shall be not less than 0.5 inches in height and in colors in contrast to the background on which they are applied. |
| 608.8.2 | **Color:** The color of pipe identification shall be discernible and consistent throughout the building. The color purple shall be used to identify reclaimed, rain and gray water distribution systems. |
| 608.15.4 | **Protection by a vacuum breaker:** The critical level of the vacuum breaker shall be set not less than 6 inches above the flood level rim of the fixture or device. |

| Section # | Highlight |
|---|---|
| | Pipe applied vacuum breakers shall be installed not less than 6 inches above the flood level rim of the fixture, receptor or device served. |
| 608.16.5 | **Connections to lawn irrigation systems:** Where systems are under continuous pressure contain chemical additives ... backflow prevention assembly or a reduced pressure principle fire protection backflow prevention assembly. |
| 610 | **Disinfection of Potable Water System** |
| 702 | **Materials** |
| 702.2 | **Underground building sanitary drainage and vent pipe:** Underground building sanitary damage and vent pipe shall conform to one of the standards listed in Table 702.2. |
| 702.5 | **Chemical waste system:** A chemical waste system shall be completely separated from the sanitary drainage system. |
| Table 702.2 | **Underground Building Drainage and Vent Pipe** |
| 704 | **Drainage Piping Installation** |
| 704.1 | **Slope of horizontal drainage piping**: Horizontal drainage piping shall be installed in uniform alignment at uniform slopes. The minimum slope of a horizontal drainage pipe shall be in accordance with Table 704.1. |
| Table 704.1 | **Slope of Horizontal Drainage Piping** |
| 705 | **Joints** |
| 705.1 | **General**: The section contains provisions applicable to joints specific to sanitary drainage piping. |
| 705.2 | **ABS plastic:** Joints between ABS plastic pipe or fittings shall comply with Sections 705.2.1 through 705.2.3. |
| 705.3 | **Asbestos cement:** Joints between asbestos-cement pipe or fittings shall be made with a sleeve coupling of the same composition as the pipe, sealed with an elastomeric ring conforming to ASTM D 1869. |
| 705.5 | **Cast iron**: Joints between cast iron pipe or fittings shall comply with sections 705.1 through 705.5.3. |
| 705.5.2 | **Compression gasket joints:** Compression gaskets for hub and spigot pipe and fittings shall conform to ASTM C 564 and shall be tested to ASTM C 1563. Gaskets shall be compressed when the pipe is fully inserted. |

| Section # | Highlight |
|---|---|
| 705.5.3 | **Mechanical joint coupling:** Mechanical joint couplings for hubless pipe and fittings shall comply with … or ASTM C 1540. |
| 705.13.2 | **Wiped:** Joints shall be fully wiped with an exposed surface on each side of the joint not less than ¾ inch. The joint shall be at least 0.325 inch thick at the thickest point. |
| 705.14.2 | **Solvent cementing:** Joint surfaces shall be clean and free from moisture. A purple primer that conforms to ASTM F 656 shall be applied. |
| 705.16 | **Polyethylene plastic pipe:** Joints between polyethylene plastic pipe and fittings shall be underground and shall comply with section 705.16.1 or 705.16.2. |
| 705.16.1 | **Heat-fusion joints:** Joints shall be undisturbed until cool. Joints shall be made in accordance with ASTM D 2657 and the manufacturer's instructions. |
| 705.16.2 | **Mechanical joints:** Mechanical joints in drainage piping shall be made with an elastomeric seal conforming to ASTM C 1173 … or CSA B602. |
| 705.17 | **Polyolefin plastic:** Joints between polyolefin plastic pipe and fittings shall comply with Sections 705.17.1 and 705.17.2. |
| 705.17.1 | **Heat-fusion joints:** Joint surfaces shall be clean and free from moisture … in accordance with ASTM F 1412 or CSA B1813. |
| 705.17.2 | **Mechanical and compression sleeve joints:** Mechanical and compression sleeve joints shall be installed in accordance with the manufacturer's instructions. |
| 705.19 | **Joints between different materials:** Joints between different piping materials shall be made with a mechanical joint of the compression or mechanical-sealing type conforming to ASTM C 1173, ASTM C 1460 or ASTM C 1461. |
| 705.19.4 | **Plastic pipe or tubing to other piping material:** Joints between different types of plastic pipe or between plastic pipe … shall be made by a caulked joint or a mechanical compression joint. |
| 705.22 | **Soldering bushings:** Soldering bushings shall be of red brass and shall be in accordance with Table 705.22. |
| Table 705.22 | **Soldering Bushing Specifications** |
| 706 | **Connections between Drainage Piping and Fittings:** |
| 706.2 | **Obstructions:** The fittings shall not have ledges, shoulders, or reductions capable of retarding or obstructing flow in the piping. Threaded drainage pipe fittings shall be of the recessed drainage type. |

| Section # | Highlight |
|---|---|
| 706.3 | **Installation of fittings:** Fittings shall be installed to guide sewage and waste in the direction of flow. Change in direction shall be made by fittings installed in accordance with Table 706.3. |
| Table 706.3 | **Fittings for Change in Direction** |
| 706.4 | **Heel- or side- inlet quarter bends:** Heel-inlet quarter bends shall be an acceptable means of connection, except where the quarter bend serves a water closet. |
| 707 | **Prohibited Joints and Connections** |
| 708 | **Cleanouts** |
| 708.3.1 | **Horizontal drains within buildings:** All horizontal drains shall be provided with cleanouts located not more than 100 feet apart. |
| 708.3.2 | **Building sewers:** Building sewers shall be provided with cleanouts located not more than 100 feet apart … at intervals of not more than 400 feet apart. |
| 708.7 | **Minimum size:** Cleanouts shall be the same nominal size as the pipe they serve up to 4 inches. For pipes larger than 4 inches nominal size, the size of the cleanout shall be not less than 4 inches. |
| 708.8 | **Clearances:** Cleanouts on 6-inch and smaller pipes shall be provided with a clearance of not less than 18-inches for rodding. Cleanouts on 8-inch and larger pipes shall be provided with a clearance of not less than 36 inches for rodding. |
| 709 | **Fixture Units** |
| 709.1 | **Values for fixtures:** Drainage fixture unit values as given in Table 709.1 designate the relative load weight … in connection with Tables 710.1(1) and 710.1(2) of sizes for soil, waste and vent pipes for which the permissible load is given in terms of fixture units. |
| 709.3 | **Values for continuous and semicontinuous flow:** Drainage fixture unit values for continuous and semicontinuous flow into s drainage system shall be computed on the basis that 1 gpm of flow is equivalent to two fixture units. |
| 710 | **Drainage System Sizing** |
| 710.1 | **Maximum fixture unit load:** The maximum number of drainage fixture units connected to a given size of building sewer … The maximum number of drainage fixture units connected to a given size horizontal branch or vertical soil or waste stack shall be determined using Table 710.(2). |
| Table 710.1(1) | **Building Drains and Sewers** |
| Table 709.1 | **Drainage Fixtures Units for Fixture Drains or Traps** |

35

| Section # | Highlight |
|---|---|
| Table 710.1(2) | **Horizontal Fixture Branches and Stacks** |
| 711 | **Offsets in Drainage Piping in Buildings of Five Stories or More** |
| 711.2 | **Horizontal stack offsets:** A stack with a horizontal offset located more than four branch intervals below the stack shall be vented in accordance with Section 907 and sized as follows: 1-3. |
| 712 | **Sumps and Ejectors** |
| 712.2 | **Valves required:** A check valve and a full open valve located on the discharge side of the check valve shall be installed in the pump or ejector discharge piping between the pump or ejector and the gravity drainage system. Access shall be provided to such valves. |
| 712.3.2 | **Sump pit** |
| 712.3.4 | **Maximum effluent level:** The effluent level control shall be adjusted and maintained …from rising within 2 inches of the invert of the gravity drain inlet into the sump. |
| 713 | **Health Care Plumbing** |
| 713.7 | **Central vacuums or disposals systems:** Where the waste from a central vacuum (fluid suction) system of the barometric-lag, collection-tank or bottle-disposal type is connected to the drainage system, the waste shall be directly connected to the sanitary drainage system through a trapped waste. |
| 713.9 | **Local vents and stacks for bedpan washers:** The local vent for a bedpan washer shall not be less than a 2-inch diameter pipe. |
| 713.9.1 | **Multiple installations:** Not more than three bedpan washers shall be connected to a 2-inch local vent stack, not more than six to a 3-inch local vent stack and not more than 12 to a 4-inch local vent stack. |
| 713.11.2 | **Boiling-type sterilizers:** The size of a sterilizer vent stack shall not be less than 2 inches in diameter where serving a utensil sterilizer not less than 1 ½ inches in diameter where serving an instrument sterilizer. |
| 802 | **Indirect Wastes** |
| 802.1 | **Where required:** All health-care related fixtures, devices and equipment shall discharge to the drainage system through an indirect waste pipe by means of an air gap in accordance with this chapter and Section 713.3. |
| 802.1.1 | **Food handling:** Equipment and fixtures utilized for the storage, preparation and handling of food shall discharge through an indirect water pipe by means of an air gap. |

| Section # | Highlight |
|---|---|
| 802.1.2 | **Floor drains in food storage areas** |
| 802.1.4 | **Swimming pools**: Where wastewater from swimming pools, backwash from filters and water from pool deck drains … the discharge shall be through an indirect waste pipe by means of an air gap. |
| 802.1.5 | **Non-potable clear-water waste:** Where devices and equipment such as process tanks, filters, drips and boilers discharge nonpotable water to the building drainage system, the discharge shall be through an indirect waste pipe by means of an air break or an air gap. |
| 802.1.7 | **Commercial dishwashing machines:** The discharge form a commercial dishwashing machine shall be through an air gap or air break in to the standpipe or waste receptor in accordance with Section 802.2. |
| 802.3 | **Waste receptors** |
| 802.3.2 | **Open hub waste receptors:** Waste receptors shall be permitted in the form of a hub or pipe extending not less than 1 inch above a water-impervious floor and are not required to have a strainer. |
| 802.4 | **Standpipes:** Standpipes shall be individually trapped. Standpipes shall extend … Access shall be provided for all standpipes and drains for rodding. |
| 804 | **Materials, Joints and Connections** |
| 902 | **Materials** |
| 902.2 | **Sheet copper:** Sheet copper for vent pipe flashings shall conform to ASTM B 152 and shall weigh not less than 8 ounces per square foot. |
| 902.3 | **Sheet lead**: Sheet lead for vent pipe flashings shall weigh not less than 3 pounds per square foot … and not less than 2 ½ pounds per square foot for prefabricated flashings. |
| 903 | **Vent Terminals** |
| 903.1 | **Roof extension:** Open vent pipes that extend through a roof shall be terminated not less than [number] inches above the roof … shall terminate not less than 7 feet above the roof. |
| 903.5 | **Location of vent terminal:** An open vent terminal from a drainage system shall not be located directly beneath any door … shall not be within 10 feet horizontally of such an opening unless it is 3 feet or more above the top of such opening. |
| 904 | **Outdoor Vent Extension** |
| 904.1 | **Required vent extension**: The vent system serving each building drain shall have at least one vent pipe that extends to the outdoors. |

| Section # | Highlight |
|---|---|
| **905** | **Vent Connections and Grades** |
| **905.5** | **Height above fixtures:** Vent terminals extending through the wall shall terminate at a point not less than 10 feet from a lot line and not less than 10 feet above average ground level. |
| **909** | **Fixture Vents** |
| **909.3** | **Crown vent**: A vent shall not be installed within two pipe diameters of the trap weir. |
| **Table 909.1** | **Maximum Distance of Fixture Trap from Vent** |
| **912** | **Wet Venting** |
| **912.1** | **Horizontal wet vent permitted:** The wet vent shall be considered the vent for the fixtures and shall extend from the connection of the dry vent along the direction of the flow in the drain pipe to the most downstream fixture drain connection to the horizontal branch drain. |
| **913** | **Waste Stack Vent** |
| **913.2** | **Stack installation:** The waste stack shall be vertical, and both horizontal and vertical offsets shall be prohibited between the lowest fixture drain connection and the highest fixture drain connection. |
| **913.4** | **Waste stack size:** The waste stack shall be sized based on the total discharge to the stack and the discharge within branch interval in accordance with Table 913.4. |
| **Table 913.4** | **Waste Stack Vent Size** |
| **914** | **Circuit Venting** |
| **914.1** | **Circuit vent permitted:** A maximum of eight fixtures connected to a horizontal branch drain shall be permitted to be circuit vented. |
| **915** | **Combination Drain and Vent System** |
| **915.1** | **Type of fixtures**: A combination drain and vent system shall not serve fixtures … combination drain and vent systems shall not receive the discharge from a food waste grinder or clinical sink. |
| **1002** | **Trap Requirements** |
| **1002.1** | **Fixture traps:** The vertical distance from the fixture outlet to the trap weir shall not exceed 24 inches, and the horizontal distance shall not exceed 30 inches measured from the centerline of the fixture outlet to the centerline of the inlet of the trap. |

| Section # | Highlight |
|-----------|-----------|
|  | A fixture shall not be double trapped. |
|  | **Exceptions:** 1 -4. |
| 1002.2 | **Design of traps:** Slip joints shall be made with an approved elastomeric gasket and shall be installed only on the trap inlet, trap outlet and within the trap seal. |
| 1002.4 | **Trap seals:** Each fixture trap shall have a liquid seal of not less than 2 inches and not more than 4 inches, or deeper for special designs relating to accessible fixtures. |
| 1003 | **Interceptors and Separators** |
| 1003.1 | **Where required:** Interceptors and separators shall be provided to prevent the discharge of oil, grease, sand and other substances harmful or hazardous to the public sewer, the private sewage system or the sewage treatment plant or processes. |
| 1003.6 | **Laundries:** Laundry facilities not installed within an individual dwelling unit or intended for individual family use … into the drainage system of solids ½ inch or larger in size, string, rags, buttons or other materials detrimental to the public sewage system. |
| 1004 | **Materials, Joints and Connections** |
| 1100 | **Storm Drainage** |
| 1102 | **Materials** |
| 1104 | **Conductors and Connections** |
| 1104.3 | **Floor Drains:** Floor drains shall not be connected to a storm drain. |
| 1106 | **Size of Conductors, Leaders and Storm Drains** |
| Table 1106.6 | **Size of Semicircular Roof Gutters** |
| 1110 | **Values for Continuous Flow** |
| 1110.1 | **Equivalent roof area**: Where there is a continuous or semicontinuous discharge … Based on rainfall rate of 1 inch per hour. |
| 1114 | **Sumps and Pumping Systems** |
| 1301 | **General** |
| 1301.2 | **Installation:** In addition to the provisions of 1301, systems for flushing of water closets and urinals shall comply with Section 1302. Except as provided for in this chapter, all systems shall comply with the other provisions of this code. |

| | |
|---|---|
| | |
| | |
| | |
| | |
| | |
| | |
| | |
| | |
| | |
| | |
| | |
| | |
| | |
| | |
| | |

# Mathematics for Plumbers and Pipefitters
## Tabs and Highlights

These 1 Exam Prep Tabs are based on the *Mathematics for Plumbers and Pipefitters, 8th Edition*.

Each Tabs sheet has five rows of tabs. Start with the first tab at the first row at the top of the page and proceed down that row placing the tabs at the locations listed below. Place each tab in your book setting it down one notch until you get to the bottom of the page, and then start back at the top again. After you have completed tabbing your book (the last tab is usually the glossary, appendix, or index), then you may start highlighting your book.

***This concludes the tabs for this book. Please continue with the highlights on the following page.***

| | |

172      **Water Measure:** A liter of water weighs 1 kilogram. One kilogram is about 2.2 pounds.

176      **Cylinders:** Volume of a cylinder formula is $V = \pi r^2 h$, or $V = 0.7854 d^2 h$

A shortcut to determine volumes of cylinders in gallons is $V = 0.0408 d^2 h$ if $d$ is measured in inches and $h$ is measured in feet.

179      **Spheres:** Volume of a sphere formula is $V = 0.5236 d^3$

190      **Ratio of Pipe Capacities:**

$$\sqrt{\left(\tfrac{D}{5}\right)^5}$$ Formula allows for friction

R = number of smaller pipes

D = diameter of larger pipes

d = diameter of smaller pipes

192      **Pipe Sizing:** Highlight: **Units of Flow for Each Pipe Size** chart

# 29 CFR 1926 OSHA
# Tabs and Highlights

These 1 Exam Prep Tabs are based on *29 CFR 1926 OSHA Construction Industry Regulations*.

Each Tabs sheet has five rows of tabs. Start with the first tab at the first row at the top of the page, and proceed down that row placing the tabs at the locations listed below. Place each tab in your book setting it down one notch until you get to the bottom of the page, and then start back at the top again. After you have completed tabbing your book (the last tab is usually the glossary, appendix, or index), then you may start highlighting your book.

*Note: Page numbers are not provided since the edition changes every six (6) months.

| 1 Exam Prep Tab | Section # |
|---|---|
| Table of Contents | ix |
| 1903: Inspections, Citations | 1903.3 |
| Citations/Penalties | 1903.14 |
| 1904: Recordkeeping Injuries | 1904.0 |
| Reporting Fatalities | 1904.39 |
| OSHA Forms | After 1904.46 |
| Access to Records | 1910.1020 (After 1926.33) |
| Noise Exposure | 1926.52 |
| Hazard Communications | 1910.1200 (or 1926.59) |
| Personal and Life Saving Equipment | Subpart E |
| Respiratory Protection | 1910.134 |
| QFLT | 1910.134(f)(6) |
| Fire Protection and Prevention | Subpart F |
| Yard Storage | 1926.151(C) |
| Signs, Signals, and Barricades | Subpart G |
| Materials Handling, Storage, Use, and Disposal | Subpart H |
| Tools - Hand and Power | Subpart I |
| Compressed Air | 1926.302(b)(4) |
| Welding and Cutting | Subpart J |
| Electrical | Subpart K |

| **1 Exam Prep Tab** | **Section #** |
| --- | --- |
| Scaffolds | Subpart L |
| Fall Protection | Subpart M |
| Roof Widths | 1926.501 (b)(10) |
| Personal Fall Arrest Systems | 1926.502(d) |
| Positioning Device Systems | 1926.502(e) |
| Fall Protection Plan | 1926.502(k) |
| Helicopters, Hoists, Elevators and Conveyors | Subpart N |
| Motor Vehicles | Subpart O |
| Excavations | Subpart P |
| Soil Classifications | Subpart P, Appendix A |
| Sloping and Benching | Subpart P, Appendix B |
| Demolition | Subpart T |
| Power Transmission and Distribution | Subpart V |
| Rollover & Overhead Protection | Subpart W |
| Stairways and Ladders | Subpart X |
| Diving | Subpart Y |
| Toxic and Hazardous Substances | Subpart Z |
| Cranes & Derricks in Construction | Subpart CC |
| 1910: General Industry Standards | 1910.12 |
| Lockout/Tagout | 1910.147 |
| Glossary | Glossary |
| Index | Index |

***This concludes the tabs for this document. Please continue with the highlights below.***

*A.M. 03/16/2021*

| Section # | Highlight |
|---|---|
| 1904.1(a)(1) | **Basic requirement:** If your company had ten 10 or fewer employees at all times during the last calendar year, you do not need to keep OSHA injury and illness records. |
| 1904.7(b)(3)(i) | **General recording criteria:** *Do I count the day on which the injury…illness began?* |
| 1904.7 (b)(3)(iv) | *How do I count weekends, holidays, or other days…work-related injury or illness.* |
| 1904.7(b)(5) | *How do I record an injury or illness that involves medical treatment beyond first aid?* |
| 1904.7(b)(5)(i) | *What is the definition of medical treatment?…does not include: Highlight (A) - (C).* |
| 1904.7(b)(5)(ii) | *What is "first aid"? Highlight* (b)(5)(ii)(A) *through* (b)(5)(ii)(N). |
| 1904.7 (b)(6) | *Is every work-related injury or illness case involving a loss of consciousness recordable?* Yes, you must…regardless of the length of time the employee remains unconscious. |
| 1904.30(a) | **Multiple business establishments – Basic requirement:** You must keep a separate OSHA log for each establishment that is expected to be in operation for one year or longer. |
| 1904.30(b) | **Implementation** |
| 1904.30(b)(1) | *Do I need to keep OSHA injury and illness records for short-term establishments(…)?* Yes, however, you do not have to…300 Log that covers all of your short-term establishments. |
| 1904.33(a) | **Retention and updating - Basic requirement:** You must save the OSHA 300 Log, the …301 Incident Report forms for five (5) years following the end of the calendar year. |
| 1904.39(a)(1) | **Reporting fatalities, hospitalizations, amputations, and losses of an eye as a result of work-related incidents to OSHA:** Within eight (8) hours after the death of any employee… to the Occupational Safety and Health Administration (OSHA), U.S. Department of Labor. |
| 1904.39(a)(2) | Within twenty-four (24) hours after the death of any employee…loss of an eye to OSHA. |
| 1926.1 | **Purpose and scope:** Highlight (a) and (b). |
| 1926.3 | **Inspections – right of entry:** Highlight (b). |
| 1926.10(a) | **Scope of Subpart:** This Subpart contains the general rules of…Secretary by regulation. |
| 1926.12(a) | **Reorganization Plan No. 14 of 1950 - General provisions:** Highlight all of (a). |
| 1926.13 | **Interpretation of statutory terms:** Highlight all of (c), (c)(1) and (c)(2). |
| 1926.15(b) | **Relationship to the Services Contract Act; The Walsh-Healy Public Contracts Act:** The Walsh-Healy Public Contracts Act…engaged in the performance of said contract." |
| 1926.16 | **Rules of construction:** Highlight (a). |
| 1926.20(a)(1) | **General safety and health provisions:** no contractor or subcontractor…health or safety. |
| 1926.20(b)(1) | It shall be the responsibility of the employer…may be necessary to comply with this Part. |
| 1926.21(b)(2) | **Safety training and education:** The employer shall…other exposure to illness or injury. |
| 1926.26 | **Illumination:** Highlight all. |
| 1926.32(d) | **Definitions: Authorized person** |

| Section # | Highlight |
|---|---|
| 1926.32(j) | **Definitions: Employee** |
| 1926.32(m) | **Definitions: Qualified** |
| 1926.32(n) | **Definitions: Safety factor** |
| 1910.1020(e)(1)(i) | **Access to records - General:** Whenever an employee…within the fifteen (15) working… of the reason for the delay and the earliest date when the record can be made available. |
| 1926.50(d)(2) | **Medical services and first aid:** The contents of the first aid kit shall be placed in a…on each job and at least weekly on each job to ensure that the expended items are replaced. |
| 1926.50 | **Appendix A First Aid Kits:** (Nonmandatory) Highlight all. |
| 1926.51(a) | **Sanitation - Potable water:** Highlight (a)(1) – (a)(6). |
| 1926.51(c)(1) | **Table D-1** for number of employees and minimum number of facilities. |
| 1926.52 | **Occupational noise exposure: Table D-2–Permissible Noise Exposures** |
| 1926.52(d)(2)(ii) | If the value of $F_e$ exceeds unity (1) the exposure exceeds permissible levels. |
| 1926.52(d)(2)(iii) | A sample computation showing an application of the formula in paragraph (d)(2)(ii) of… Since the value of $F_e$ does not exceed unity, the exposure is within permissible limits. |
| 1926.52(e) | Exposure to impulsive or impact noise should not exceed 140 dB peak sound pressure level. |
| 1926.55 | **Gases, vapors, fumes, dusts, and mists:** Review Appendix A – Threshold Limit Values of Airborne Contaminants for Construction. |
| 1926.56 | **Illumination: Table D-3 Minimum Illumination Intensities in Foot-Candles** |
| 1926.57(b) | **Ventilation - Local exhaust ventilation** |
| 1926.57(d)(2) | **Duration of operations:** Since dust capable of causing disability is, according to the… equipment should not remove same immediately until the atmosphere seems clear. |
| 1926.57(f)(1)(vi) | **Clean air:** Air of such purity that it will not cause harm or discomfort to an individual if it is inhaled for extended periods of time. |
| 1926.57(f)(2)(ii) | **Dust hazards from abrasive blasting:** The concentration of respirable dust…of this Part. |
| 1926.57(f)(3)(i) | **Blast-cleaning enclosures:** Blast-cleaning enclosures shall be exhaust ventilated in such a way that a continuous inward flow of air will be maintained at all openings in the enclosure during the blasting operation. |
| 1926.57(f)(5)(ii) | **Personal protective equipment:** Abrasive-blasting respirators shall be worn by abrasive-blasting operators: Highlight (A), (B), and (C). |
| 1926.60 | **Methylenedianiline – Scope and application:** (a)(1) This Section applies to all construction…including but not limited to the following: Highlight (i), (ii), (iii), and (iv). |
| 1926.60(b) | **Definitions: 4,4' Methylenedianiline or MDA** |
| 1926.60(c) | **Permissible exposure limits** |

| Section # | Highlight |
|---|---|
| 1926.60(f)(1)(ii) | **Exposure monitoring:** Representative employee shall be determined on the basis of... shift for each job classification in each work area where exposure to MDA may occur. |
| 1926.60(h)(5)(i) | **Compliance program:** The employer shall establish and implement a written program to reduce employee exposure to or below the PELs by means of engineering and work... (1) of this Section, and by use of respiratory protection where permitted under this Section. |
| 1926.60(j)(2)(iv) | **Removal and storage:** MDA-contaminated work clothing or equipment shall be placed ...and transported in sealed, impermeable bags, or other closed impermeable containers. |
| 1926.60(l)(2) | **Signs and labels - Signs:** Highlight (l)(2)(i) thru (l)(2)(ii)(B)(2). |
| 1926.60(n)(9)(vi) | **Medical removal protection benefits:** Voluntary removal or restriction of an employee. Where an employee, although not required by this Section to do so, removes an employee... benefits to the employee equal to that required by paragraph (n)(9)(v) of this Section. |
| 1926.62(a) | **Lead - Scope:** Construction work is defined as work for construction, alteration and /or repair, including painting and decorating. It includes but is not limited to the following: Highlight: (a)(1) – (a)(7). |
| 1926.62(c)(1) | **Permissible exposure limit:** The employer shall assure that no employee is exposed to lead at concentration greater than fifty micrograms per cubic meter of air (50 ug/m$^3$) averaged over an 8-hour period. |
| 1926.62(d)(6)(ii) | **Frequency:** If the initial determination or subsequent determination reveals employee... for that employee except as otherwise provided in paragraph (d)(7) of this Section. |
| 1926.62(f)(1) | **Respiratory protection - General:** the employer must provide employee an appropriate respirator that complies with the requirements of the paragraph. Respirators must be used during: Highlight (i) thru (iv). |
| 1926.62(j)(2) | **Biological monitoring:** Highlight (j)(2)(i) – (j)(2)(i)(C). |
| 1926.62(j)(2)(iv) | **Employee notification:** Highlight (j)(2)(iv)(A) and (B). |
| 1926.65 | **Appendix C 1. Occupational Safety and Health Program:** Highlight section. |
| 1926.95(a) | **Criteria for personal protective equipment - Application:** Protective equipment, including personal protective equipment for eyes, face, head, and extremities, protective... the function of any part of the body through absorption, inhalation or physical contact. |
| 1926.95(b) | **Employer-owned equipment:** Where employees provide their own protective equipment, the employer shall be responsible to assure its adequacy, including proper maintenance, and sanitation of such equipment. |
| 1926.100 | **Head protection:** Highlight all. |
| 1926.102(a)(5) | **Eye and face protection:** Protectors shall meet the following requirements: (i) – (vi). |
| 1910.134(b) | **Respiratory protection - Definitions: Escape-only respirator** means a respirator intended to be used only for emergency exits. |
| 1910.134(f)(6) | QLFT may only be used to fit test negative pressure air purifying respirators that must achieve a fit factor of 100 or less. |
| 1926.104 | **Safety belts, lifelines, and lanyards:** Highlight (a) – (f). |

| Section # | Highlight |
|---|---|
| 1926.105(c)(1) | **Safety nets:** Nets shall extend 8 feet beyond the edge of the work surface where employees …the work surface as practical but in no case more than 25 feet below such work surface. |
| 1926.106 | **Working over or near water:** Highlight (a) – (d). |
| 1926.150(b)(1) | **Fire protection – Water supply:** A temporary or permanent water supply, of sufficient… equipment shall be made available as soon as combustible materials accumulate. |
| 1926.150(c)(1)(vi) | **Portable firefighting equipment:** A fire extinguisher, rated not less than 10B, shall be provided…This requirement does not apply to the integral fuel tanks of motor vehicles. |
| 1926.150(d)(2) | **Standpipes:** In all structures in which standpipes are required, or where standpipes… conspicuously marked. There shall be at least one standard hose outlet at each floor. |
| 1926.151 | **Fire prevention: Table F-1–Fire Extinguishers Data** |
| 1926.151(c)(2) | **Open yard storage:** Driveways between and around combustible storage piles shall be… free from accumulation of rubbish, equipment, or other articles or materials. Driveways shall be so spaced that a maximum grid system unit of 50 feet x 150 feet is produced. |
| 1926.152(d)(1) | **Flammable liquids – Fire control for flammable liquid storage:** At least one portable fire extinguisher…into any room used for storage of more than 60 gallons of flammable liquids. |
| 1926.153 | **Liquefied petroleum gas (LP-Gas):** Includes handling and storage as well as container. Specifications, **Table F-3** & **Table F-31** Storage of LP-gas. |
| 1926.154 | **Temporary heating devices: Table F-4** |
| 1926.200(d) | **Accident prevention signs and tags – Exit signs:** Exit signs, when required, shall be lettered in legible red letters, not less than 6 inches high, on a white field and the principal stroke of the letters shall be at least three-fourths inch in width. |
| 1926.200(h)(1) | **Accident prevention tags:** Accident prevention tags shall be used as a temporary means of warning employees of an existing hazard, such as defective tools, equipment, etc. They shall not be used in place of, or as a substitute for, accident prevention signs. |
| 1926.250(b) | **General requirements for storage - Material storage:** Highlight (b)(1) thru (b)(7). |
| 1926.251(a)(6) | **Rigging equipment and material handling – Inspections:** Each day before being used …warrant. Damaged or defective slings shall be immediately removed from service. |
| 1926.251(d) | **Natural rope, and synthetic fiber:** Highlight (d)(1) and all of (d)(2) including (i) – (v). |
| 1926.251(d)(3) | **Safe operating temperatures:** Highlight all. |
| 1926.251 | **Table H-1 Maximum Allowable Wear at any Point of Link** |
| | **Table H-2 Number and Spacing of U-Bolt Wire Rope Clips** |
| 1926.252(a) | **Disposal of waste materials:** Whenever materials are dropped more than 20 feet to any point lying outside the exterior walls of the building, an enclosed chute of wood, or… closed in on all sides, through which material is moved from a high place to a lower one. |
| 1926.300(b)(4)(iv) | **General requirements - Point of operation guarding:** The following are some of the machines which usually require point of operation guarding: Highlight (A) – (I). |

| Section # | Highlight |
|---|---|
| 1926.300(d)(3) | **Switches:** All other hand-held powered tools, such as circular saws, chain saws, and… with a constant pressure switch that will shut off the power when the pressure is released. |
| 1926.301 | **Hand tools:** Highlight all. |
| 1926.302(b)(3) | **Power-operated hand tools:** Highlight all. |
| 1926.302(b)(4) | **Power-operated hand tools:** Highlight all. |
| 1926.302(b)(6) | The use of hoses for hoisting or lowering tools shall not be permitted. |
| 1926.303(b)(1) | **Abrasive wheels and tools - Guarding:** Grinding machines shall be equipped with safety… for the Use, Care and Protection of Abrasive Wheels, and paragraph (d) of this Section. |
| 1926.303(c)(5) | **Use of abrasive wheels:** Highlight all. |
| 1926.304(d) | **Woodworking tools – Guarding:** Highlight all. |
| 1926.305(c) | **Jacks–lever and ratchet, screw, and hydraulic - Blocking:** Highlight all. |
| 1926.350(a)(1) | **Gas welding and cutting - Transporting, moving, and storing compressed gas cylinders:** Valve protection caps shall be in place and secured. |
| 1926.350(a)(10) | Oxygen cylinders in storage shall be separated from fuel-gas cylinders or combustible… barrier at least 5 feet high having a fire resistance rating of at least one-half hour. |
| 1926.350(d) | **Use of fuel gas:** The employer shall thoroughly instruct employees in the safe use of fuel gas, as follows: Highlight all (d)(1) thru (d)(6). |
| 1926.350(e)(2) | **Fuel gas and oxygen manifolds:** Fuel gas and oxygen manifolds shall be placed in safe, well ventilated, accessible locations. They shall not be located within enclosed spaces. |
| 1926.351(d) | **Arc welding and cutting - Operating instructions:** Employers shall instruct employees in the safe means of arc welding and cutting as follows: Highlight (d)(1) thru (d)(5). |
| 1926.354(a) | **Welding, cutting, and heating in way of preservation coatings:** Before welding cutting or heating is commenced on…made by a competent person to determine its flammability. |
| 1926.403(i)(1) | **General requirements – Working space about electric equipment:** Highlight all. |
| 1926.403(i)(1)(i) | **Working clearances:** Highlight all. |
| 1926.403 | **Table K-1 Working Clearances** |
| | **Table K-2 Minimum Depth of Clear Working Space in Front of Electric Equip.** |
| | **Table K-3 Elevation of Unguarded Energized Parts Above Working Space** |
| 1926.404(b)(1) | **Branch circuits - Ground-fault protection:** Highlight (b)(1)(i) – (b)(1)(ii). |
| 1926.404(b)(1)(iii)(E) | All required tests shall be performed: Highlight (E)(1) – (E)(4). |
| 1926.404 | **Table K-4 Receptacle Ratings for Various Size Circuits** |
| 1926.405(a)(1)(ii) | **Wiring methods, components, and equipment for general use - Wiring in ducts:** Highlight all. |
| 1926.405(j) | **Equipment for general use:** Highlight all (j)(1) thru (j)(1)(v). |

| Section # | Highlight |
|---|---|
| 1926.405(j)(2) | **Receptacles, cord, connectors, and attachment plugs (caps):** Highlight thru (j)(2)(i) – (ii). |
| 1926.407(a) | **Hazardous (classified) locations - Scope:** Highlight all. |
| 1926.408(c)(4) | **Special systems - Equipment location:** Highlight all. |
| 1926.450(b) | **Scope, application, and definitions applicable to this Subpart - Definitions:** Review |
| 1926.451(a) | **General requirements - Capacity:** Highlight (a)(1), (a)(4), (a)(5), and (a)(6). |
| 1926.451(b) | **Scaffold platform construction:** Highlight (b)(1) – (b)(5)(ii). |
| 1926.451(c)(1) | **Criteria for supported scaffolds:** Supported scaffolds with height to base width (including outrigger supports, if used) ratio of more than four to one (4:1) shall be restrained from tipping by guying, tying, bracing, or equivalent means, as follows: Highlight (i) – (iii). |
| 1926.451(d)(3) | **Criteria for suspension scaffolds:** Highlight all. |
| 1926.451(d)(3)(viii) | Outrigger beams shall be placed perpendicular to its bearing support (usually the face… beam may be placed at some other angle, provided the opposing angle tiebacks are used. |
| 1926.451(e) | **Access:** Highlight (e) and (e)(1). |
| 1926.451(e)(2)(v) | Hook-on and attachable ladders shall have a minimum rung length of 11 ½ inches; and |
| 1926.451(e)(3) | Stairway-type ladders shall: Highlight (i) – (iv). |
| 1926.451(g)(1) | **Fall protection:** Each employee on a scaffold more than 10 feet above a lower level shall be protected from falling to that lower level. |
| 1926.451(g)(1)(iii) | **Fall protection:** Highlight all. |
| 1926.451(g)(3)(ii) | **Fall protection:** Highlight all. |
| 1926.451(g)(4)(vii) | **Fall protection:** Highlight all. |
| 1926.451(h)(2)(ii) | **Falling object protection:** Highlight all. |
| 1926.452 | **Additional requirements applicable to specific types of scaffolds:**<br>**(a) Pole scaffolds**<br>**(b) Tube and coupler scaffolds**<br>**(c) Fabricated frame scaffolds (tubular welded frame scaffolds)**<br>(c)(6) Scaffolds over 125 feet in height above their base shall be…with such design.<br>**(d) Plasterers', decorators', and large area scaffolds**<br>**(e) Bricklayers' square scaffolds (squares)**<br>**(f) Horse scaffolds**<br>**(g) Form scaffolds and carpenters' bracket scaffolds**<br>**(h) Roof bracket scaffolds**<br>**(i) Outrigger scaffolds**<br>**(j) Pump jack scaffold**<br>**(k) Ladder jack scaffold**<br>**(l) Window jack scaffold**<br>**(m) Crawling boards (chicken ladders)**<br>**(n) Step, platform, and trestle ladder scaffolds**<br>**(o) Single-point adjustable suspension scaffolds** |

| Section # | Highlight |
|---|---|
| | (p) **Two-point adjustable suspension scaffolds (swing stages)** |
| | (q) **Multi-point adjustable suspension scaffolds, stonesetters'…, and masons'…** |
| | (r) **Catenary scaffolds** |
| | (s) **Float (ship) scaffolds** |
| | (t) **Interior hung scaffolds** |
| | (u) **Needle beam scaffolds** |
| | (v) **Multi-level suspended scaffolds** |
| | (w) **Mobile scaffolds** |
| | (x) **Repair bracket scaffolds** |
| | (y) **Stilts** |

1926.453(b)  **Aerial lifts - Specific requirements - Ladder trucks and tower trucks:** Highlight (b)(1).

1926.454  **Training requirements:** Highlight all including (a) – (a)(5).

Appendix A  **Subpart L Appendix A Scaffold specifications:** *Note: This is indicating where more detail can be found for scaffolding which was defined above.* Highlight the two **Tables** under **1. Guidelines and Tables:** maximum intended nominal load (*this table correlates load with thickness for dressed and undressed lumber rated capacity*).

1926.500(b)  **Scope, application, and definitions applicable to this Subpart - Definitions:** Review.

1926.501(b)(1)  **Duty to have fall protection - Unprotected sides and edges:** Highlight all.

1926.501(b)(10) **Roofing work on low-slope roofs:** Highlight all.

1926.501(b)(15) **Walking/working surfaces not otherwise addressed:** Highlight all.

1926.501(c)  **Protection from falling objects:** When an employee is exposed to falling objects, the employer…hat and shall implement one of the following measures: Highlight (c)(1) – (c)(3).

1926.502(b)(1)  **Fall protection criteria and practices - Guardrail systems:** Highlight all.

1926.502(b)(2)  Highlight all.

1926.502(b)(2)(iv)  Highlight all.

1926.502(b)(3)  Highlight all.

1926.502(b)(4)  Highlight all.

1926.502(b)(9)  Highlight all.

1926.502(c)(1)  **Safety net systems:** Safety nets shall be installed as close as practicable under the walking …which employees are working, but in no case more than 30 feet (9.1 m) below such level.

1926.502(d)  **Personal fall arrest systems:** Highlight all.

1926.502(d)(9)  Lanyards and vertical lifelines shall have a minimum breaking strength of 5,000 pounds (22.2kN).

1926.502(d)(12) Self-retracting lifelines and lanyards which do not limit free fall distance to 2 feet or less shall be capable of sustaining a minimum tensile load of 3,000 pounds…extended position.

1926.502(d)(15) Anchorages used for attachment of personal fall arrest equipment shall be…being used to support or suspend platforms and capable of supporting at least 5,000 pounds (22.2 kN).

| | |
|---|---|

| Section # | Highlight |
|---|---|
| 1926.652(b) | **Requirements for protective systems - Design of sloping and benching systems** |
| 1926.652(b)(1) | **Option (1)** Allowable configurations and slopes. |
| 1926.652(b)(2) | **Option (2)** Determination of slopes and configurations using Appendices A and B. |
| 1926.652(b)(3) | **Option (3)** Designs using other tabulated data. |
| 1926.652(b)(4) | **Option (4)** Design by a registered professional engineer. |
| Subpart P(b) | **Appendix A Soil classification - Definitions: Submerged soil** means soil which is under water or is free seeping. |
| | **Type A** means cohesive soils with an unconfined compressive strength of 1.5 ton per square foot (tsf) (144 kPa) or greater. Examples of cohesive soils are: clay, silty clay, sandy clay, clay loam…considered Type A. However, no soil is Type A if: Highlight (i) – (v). |
| | **Type B** means: Highlight (i) – (vi). |
| | **Type C** means: Highlight (i) – (v). |
| Subpart P | **Appendix B Sloping and benching:** *This section provides pictorial descriptions of run to rise calculations. Also* **Figure B-1** *which relates the types of soil to the required run to rise (horizontal to vertical) ratio to determine the amount of slope.* |
| (b) | **Definitions: Distress** means that the soil is in a condition where a cave-in is imminent or is likely to occur. Distress is evidenced by such phenomena as the development of fissures in the face of adjacent to an open excavation; the subsidence of the edge of an excavation; the slumping of material from the face or the bulging. |
| (3)(ii) | **Actual Slope:** The actual slope shall be less steep than the maximum allowable slope, when there are signs of distress. If that situation occurs, the slope shall be cut back to an actual slope which is at least 1/2 horizontal to one vertical (1/2 H:1V) less steep than the maximum allowable slope. |
| (4) | **Configurations:** Configurations of sloping and benching systems shall be in accordance with Figure B-1. |
| | Highlight: **Figure B-1 Slope Configurations** and #3 under the Notes. |
| Subpart P | **Appendix C Timber shoring for trenches:** Tables **C-1.1** through **C-2.3** |
| Subpart P | **Appendix D Aluminum hydraulic shoring for trenches:** Tables **D-1.1** through **D-1.4** These are aluminum shoring components flow charts. |
| 1926.700(b) | **Definitions applicable to this Subpart:** Highlight (b)(1) – (b)(9). |
| 1926.702(b) | **Requirements for equipment and tools - Concrete mixers.** Concrete mixers with one cubic yard or larger loading skips shall be equipped with the following: (b)(1) – (b)(2). |
| 1926.702(c) | **Power concrete trowels:** equipped with a control switch that will automatically shut off the power whenever the hands of the operator are removed from the equipment handles. |
| 1926.702(j) | **Lockout/Tagout procedures** |
| 1926.703(b) | **Shoring and reshoring** |

| Section # | Highlight |
|-----------|-----------|
| 1926.706(a) | **Requirements for masonry construction:** A limited access zone shall be established... The limited access zone shall conform to the following: Highlight (a)(1) – (a)(5). |
| 1926.706(b) | All masonry walls over 8 ft. in height shall be adequately braced to prevent overturning... shall remain in place until permanent supporting elements of the structure are in place. |
| 1926.751 | **Definitions:** Review. |
| 1926.754 | **Structural steel assembly** |
| 1926.754(b)(2) | **The following additional requirements shall apply for multi-story structures:** At no time shall there be more than four floors or 48 feet...maintained as a result of the design. |
| 1926.852(b) | **Chutes:** The openings shall not exceed 48 inches in height measured along the wall of the chute. |
| 1926.859(b) | **Mechanical demolition:** The weight of the demolition ball shall not exceed 50 percent or the cranes rated load...line by which it is suspended, whichever results in a lesser value. |
| 1926.968 | **Definitions: Barricade** and **Barrier** |
| 1926.1050(b) | **Definitions:** Review. |
| 1926.1051(a) | **General requirements:** A stairway or ladder shall be provided at all...19 inches or more. |
| 1926.1051(a)(2) | A double-cleated ladder or two or more separate ladders shall be provided when ladders... 25 or more employees, or when a ladder is to serve simultaneous two-way traffic. |
| 1926.1052(a)(1) | **Stairways:** have landings of not less than 30 inches in the...and extend at least 22 inches. |
| 1926.1052(a)(3) | Variations in riser height and tread depth shall not be over ¼-inch in any stairway system. |
| 1926.1052(c)(1) | **Stairrails and handrails:** Stairways having four or more risers or rising more than 30... shall be equipped with: (i) At least one handrail; and (ii) One stair rail system along each unprotected side or edge. |
| 1926.1052(c)(11) | Handrails that will not be permanent part of the structure being built shall have a minimum clearance of 3 inches...handrail and walls, stairrail systems, and other objects. |
| 1926.1053(a)(1) | **Ladders:** Ladders shall be capable of supporting the following loads without failure: Highlight: (i) – (iii). |
| 1926.1053(a)(3)(i) | Rungs, cleats, and steps of portable ladders and fixed ladders shall be spaced not less than 10 inches nor more than 14 inches apart. |
| 1926.1053(a)(3)(ii) | Rungs, cleats, and steps of step stools...not less than 8 inches apart, nor more than 12 inches ...as measured between center lines of the rungs, cleats, and steps. |
| 1926.1053(a)(3)(iii) | Rungs, cleats, and steps of the base section of extension trestle ladders shall be not less... as measured between center lines of the rungs, cleats, and steps. |
| 1926.1053(a)(4)(i) | The minimum clear distance between sides of individual rung/step...shall be 16 inches. |
| 1926.1053(a)(6)(i) | The rungs and steps of fixed metal ladders...otherwise treated to minimize slipping. |
| 1926.1053(a)(7) | Ladders shall not be tied or fastened together...are specifically designed for such use. |

| Section # | Highlight |
|---|---|
| 1926.1053(a)(8) | A metal spreader or locking device shall be provided on each stepladder to hold the front and back sections in an open position when the ladder is being used. |
| 1926.1053(a)(13) | The minimum perpendicular clearance between fixed ladder rungs, cleats, and steps and… for which a minimum perpendicular clearance of 4½ inches (11 cm) is required. |
| 1926.1053(a)(19) | Where the total length of a climb equals or exceeds 24 feet…the following: (i) – (iii). |
| 1926.1053(a)(21) | Wells for fixed ladders shall conform to all of the following: (i) – (v). |
| 1926.1053(a)(22) | Ladder safety devices, and related…shall conform to all of the following: (i) – (iv). |
| 1926.1053(a)(24) | The side rails of a through or sidestep fixed ladders shall extend 42 inches above the top of the access level or landing platform…the access level shall be the top of the parapet. |
| 1926.1053(b)(1) | **Use:** When portable ladders are used for access to an upper landing surface, the ladder side rails shall extend at least 3 feet…by itself, cause the ladder to slip off its support. |
| 1926.1053(b)(5)(i) | Non-self-supporting…used at an angle such that the horizontal distance from the top support to the foot of the ladder is approx. one quarter the working length of the ladder. |
| 1926.1053(b)(5)(ii) | Wood job made ladders with spliced side rails shall be used at an angle that is one-eighth the working length of the ladder. |
| 1926.1101(b) | **Asbestos - Definitions:** Review. |
| 1926.1101(c) | **Permissible exposure limits (PELS)** |
| 1926.1101(c)(1) | **Time-weighted average limit (TWA):** The employer shall ensure that no employee is exposed to an airborne concentration of asbestos in excess of 0.1 fiber per cubic centimeter of air as an eight-hour time-weighted average…or by an equivalent method. |
| 1926.1101(g)(8) | **Additional Controls for Class II work:** Highlight all. |
| 1926.1101(g)(8)(i) | For removing vinyl and asphalt flooring materials…these practices pursuant to paragraph (k)(9) of this Section: (i)(A) – (i)(I). |
| 1926.1101(g)(8)(ii) | For removing roofing material which…following work practices are followed: (A) – (H). |
| 1926.1101(g)(8)(iii) | When removing cementitious asbestos-containing siding and shingles or transite panels… the employer shall ensure that the following work practices are followed: (A) – (D). |
| 1926.1101(g)(8)(iv) | When removing gaskets containing ACM…work practices are followed: (A) – (D). |
| 1926.1101(g)(8)(v) | When performing any other Class II removal of asbestos containing material for which specific controls have not been…following work practices are complied with. (A) – (D). |
| 1926.1101(g)(8)(vi) | **Alternative Work Practices and Controls:** Instead of the work practices and controls… the following provisions are complied with. (A) – (B). |
| 1926.1101(h)(3)(ii) | **Respirator protection:** Employers must provide an employee with tight-fitting, powered… the employee chooses to use a PAPR and it provides adequate protection to the employee. |
| 1926.1101(h)(3)(iii) | Employers must provide employees with an air-purifying half mask respirator, other… whenever employees perform: Highlight (A) – (B). |

| Section # | Highlight |
|---|---|
| 1926.1101(j) | **Hygiene facilities and practices for employees:** Requirements for employees performing Class I…25 linear or 10 square feet of TSI or surfacing ACM and PACM. |
| 1926.1101(j)(1)(i) | **Decontamination areas:** regulated area through the decontamination area. |
| 1926.1101(j)(1)(i)(A) | **Equipment room:** Highlight all. |
| 1926.1101(j)(1)(i)(B) | **Shower area:** Highlight all. |
| 1926.1101(j)(1)(i)(C) | **Clean change room:** Highlight all. |
| 1926.1400 | **Scope** |
| 1926.1401 | **Definitions:** Review. |
| 1910.147 | **The control of hazardous energy (lockout/tagout)** |

# 1 Exam Prep
## International Fuel Gas Code
## Questions and Answers

1. A gas appliance is located in a confined space and has a clearance on the sides and back of 1" and 6" at the front. What is the minimum number of permanent openings required for the space to communicate with the outdoors?

   A. One
   B. Two
   C. Three
   D. Four

2. A single category I appliance has a gas demand of 98,000 btu/h. What is the maximum horizontal run for the double wall Type B vent if it has a vertical run of 30 feet?

   A. 30'
   B. 35'
   C. 40'
   D. 50'

3. When is a venting system permitted to pass through a furnace plenum?

   A. Not permitted
   B. When protected
   C. When the furnace is less than 50,000 btu/h
   D. None of the above

4. The radius of the inner curve of plastic piping bends shall not be less than_____ the inside diameter of the pipe.

   A. 25 times
   B. 10 times
   C. 5 times
   D. 18 times

5. An appliance has a demand of 80,000 btu/h. It is communicating directly with the outdoors. What is the minimum net free area of each opening?

   A. 80 sq in
   B. 40 sq in
   C. 20 sq in
   D. 100 sq in
   E.

6. What is the minimum thickness for an 18 inch steel vent connector for a medium heat appliance?

A. 0.089 inch
B. 0.093 inch
C. 0.097 inch
D. 0.101 inch

7. Which of the following metallic pipes is NOT permitted to be used for gas piping?

A. Cast-iron
B. Steel
C. Copper
D. Aluminum

8. How long is a 2000 cubic foot gas piping system required to be tested for?

A. ½ hour
B. 2 hours
C. 4 hours
D. 24 hours

9. A plumbing vent outlet is discharging 2 feet above a forced-air warm-air furnace outside air inlet. What is the minimum distance that the outside air inlet shall be from the vent outlet?

A. 10 feet
B. 12 feet
C. 15 feet
D. 20 feet

10. What is the approximate gas input rating for a Refrigerator?

A. 2,500 btu/h
B. 3,000 btu/h
C. 3,500 btu/h
D. 4,000 btu/h

11. No portion of a venting system shall pass through any circulation air duct or _____.

A. Furnace plenum
B. Framed Wall
C. Attic
D. Crawl space

12. An appliance has a demand of 160,000 btu/h. It is communicating with the outdoors through vertical openings. What is the minimum net free area of each opening?

A. 40 sq in
B. 100 sq in
C. 160 sq in
D. 80 sq in

13. How far shall a gas vent extend above a roof of a house when the roof has a slope of 9/12?

A. 2 feet
B. 2 ½ feet
C. 4 feet
D. 5 feet

14. What is the required vertical clearance from combustible construction for a vent that is protect with 0.024 sheet metal with ventilated airspace? The required clearance with no protection is 18".

A. 6 inches
B. 9 inches
C. 18 inches
D. 24 inches

15. A drip is place at what point in a system of piping to collect condesate?

A. Low
B. Mid
C. High
D. Average

16. What is the minimum distance from combustible construction for medium heat equipment from a single-wall metal pipe?

A. 36"
B. 24"
C. 6"
D. 9"

17. When the vent connector used for equipment having a draft hood passes through an attic, what material shall that portion of the vent be?

A. Type B or L
B. Type B
C. Type L
D. None of the above

18. Joint compounds, which act as a lubricant and sealant, are applied to male threads only and shall be resistant to the action of what?

A. LP gas
B. Nat gas
C. Medical gas
D. None of the shown

19. When gas piping is in solid floors and both ends terminates outdoors, how far shall the casing (conduit) extend beyond the point where the pipe emerges from the floor?

A. 2 inches
B. 3 inches
C. 1 inch
D. 4 inches

20. For gas piping underground beneath buildings, how far shall the conduit for gas piping extend outside of a building when one end terminate outdoors?

A. 2"
B. 4"
C. 8"
D. 1"

21. An appliance has a demand of 110,000 btu/h. It is using indoor air for combustion air. What is the minimum net free area of each opening?

A. 110 sq in
B. 100 sq in
C. 80 sq in

22. What is the minimum burial depth underground gas piping?

A. 12"
B. 24"
C. 16"
D. 18"

23. What is the minimum distance that shield plates shall extend above sole plates for gas piping?

A. 2"
B. 4"
C. 6"
D. 8"

24. What is the minimum height of a cleanout on a masonry chimney flue?

A. 4"
B. 6"
C. 9"
D. 12"

25. What is the minimum melting temperature for brazing material?

A. 1000 degrees Fahrenheit
B. 800 degrees Fahrenheit
C. 1200 degrees Fahrenheit
D. 600 degrees Fahrenheit

26. Which of the following pipe joints is not permitted for gas piping?

A. Soldering
B. Threading
C. Brazing
D. Welding

27. Which of the following codes regulates the storage for liquefied petroleum gas?

A. NFPA 58
B. IFGC
C. IBC
D. IMC

28. What is the maximum spacing of supports for 1 inch gas pipe that is hung horizontally?

A. 6 feet
B. 8 feet
C. 10 feet
D. 12 feet

29. What is the maximum bend of metallic gas pipe?

A. 30 degrees
B. 45 degrees
C. 60 degrees
D. 90 degrees

30. What is the maximum support spacing for ¾ inch gas tubing that is hung horizontally?

A. 6 feet
B. 8 feet
C. 10 feet
D. 12 feet

31. Where shall a sediment trap be located if it is not part of the gas utilization equipment, where shall it be installed?

A. As close to the inlet of the equipment as practical
B. As close to the outlet of the equipment as practical
C. As far from the inlet of the equipment as practical
D. As far from the outlet of the equipment as practical

32. Which of the following is true regarding thread compounds?

A. Shall be resistant to the action to the action of lp gas
B. Shall serve as a anti-corrosive substance
C. Shall be applied to the female threads only
D. None of the above

33. When is a gas piping system design operating pressure allowed to exceed 5 psig?

A. When the system is welded
B. When the system is soldered
C. When the piping is a permanent installation
D. When the system serves all parts of a building

34. Approximately how many threads are to be cut on 4" iron gas pipe?

A. 10
B. 11
C. 12
D. 13

35. When is a venting system permitted to pass through a furnace plenum?

A. Not permitted
B. When protected
C. When the furnace is less than 50,000 btu/h
D. None of the above

36. Unvented room heaters shall be equipped with an_____sensitive safety shutoff system.

A. Oxygen
B. Air
C. Nitrogen
D. Carbon

37. An appliance is communicating through outdoors through horizontal ducts. The demand is 120,000 btu/h. Which of following metal louver dimensions not allowed for combustion air?

A. 2" x 40"
B. 4" x 20"
C. 5" x 16"
D. 8" x 10"

38. What is the minimum clearance at the back for a floor-mounted-type unit heater to combustible materials?

A. 6"
B. 12"
C. 18"
D. 24"

39. A drip is place at what point in a system of piping to collect condensate?

A. Low
B. Mid
C. High
D. Average

40. According to the International Fuel Gas Code, boilers shall be listed in accordance with the requirements of _____.

A. ANSI Z21.13
B. UL 895
C. NSF/ANSI 50
D. ASTM C842-05

# 1 Exam Prep
## International Fuel Gas Code
## Answers

| | | |
|---|---|---|
| 1. | A | 304.6.2 |
| 2. | A | 504.2 (1) |
| 3. | A | 503.3.5 |
| 4. | A | 405.3 |
| 5. | C | 304.6.1 |
| 6. | B | 503.10.2.5 |
| 7. | A | 403.4.1 |
| 8. | B | 406.4.2 |
| 9. | A | 618.4 (1) |
| 10. | B | 402.2 |
| 11. | A | 503.3.5 |
| 12. | A | 304.6.1 |
| 13. | A | 503.6.4 |
| 14. | B | 308.2 |
| 15. | A | 202 |
| 16. | A | 503.10.5 |
| 17. | A | 503.10.2.2 |
| 18. | A | 403.9.3 |
| 19. | A | 404.8.2 |
| 20. | B | 404.14.1 |
| 21. | A | 304.5.3.1 |
| 22. | A | 404.12 |
| 23. | B | 404.7 |
| 24. | B | 501.15.3 |
| 25. | A | 202 |
| 26. | A | 403.10.1 |
| 27. | A | 401.2 |
| 28. | B | 415.1 |
| 29. | D | 405.2 |
| 30. | A | 415.1 |
| 31. | A | 408.4 |
| 32. | A | 403.9.3 |
| 33. | A | 402.6 |
| 34. | D | 403.9.2 |
| 35. | A | 503.3.5 |
| 36. | A | 621.6 |
| 37. | A | 304.6.1 (Ducts cannot be less in 3") |
| 38. | A | 620.4 |
| 39. | A | 202 |
| 40. | A | 631.1 |

# Mathematics for Plumbers and Pipefitters, 8th Edition
# Questions and Answers

1. The vertex of an angle is the _____ of a circle and the angle is formed by _____ lines.

    A. Diameter, radius
    B. Radius, various
    C. Center, radius
    D. Circumference, given

2. _____ drainage fittings have inside construction designed to cause little turbulence.

    A. Tee
    B. Tee Wye
    C. Wye
    D. Ell

3. The cast iron fitting that is used in a way similar to the threaded ell is called a/an _____.

    A. Curve
    B. Arc
    C. Bend
    D. Elbow

4. To compute volume in cubic inches, the Bureau of Standards uses _____ cubic inches as 1 gallon.

    A. 27
    B. 231
    C. 213
    D. 7.48

5. In plumbing, water pressure is measured by gauge, height, or by _____ pressure, in feet.

    A. Head
    B. Crown
    C. Peak
    D. Vertex

6. _____ is not a cast iron pipe connection.

    A. Compression gaskets
    B. No-hub joints
    C. Lead and oakum joints
    D. Soldered joints

7. A _____ is waste and vent piping to connect a fixture at some distance from a stack.

    A. Loop
    B. Hook
    C. Curve
    D. Circuit

8. Parallel offsets always have _____ and are used because of a neat appearance.

    A. Running offsets
    B. Double offsets
    C. Parallel angles one-half of the offset angle
    D. Offset angles one-half the size of the parallel angles

9. _____ method is used to check pipe length calculations when there is no math constant.

    A. Scale-checker
    B. Trial and error
    C. Lay-out
    D. A pipe length device

10. _____ offsets go around a stack or tank and have diagonals, which are always 45 degrees.

    A. Diagonal
    B. Jumper
    C. Tee-wye
    D. Elbow

11. When a 13'- 8" long pipe is cut into 3 equal segments, each is approximately _____ long.

    A. 4'- 5 3/16"
    B. 4'- 5 7/16"
    C. 4'- 6 5/8"
    D. 4'- 7 5/16"

12. When a 21'- 1" long pipe is cut into 4 equal segments, each is approximately _____ long.

    A. 5'- 2 5/8"
    B. 5'- 3 1/4"
    C. 5'- 3 5/8"
    D. 5'- 3 7/8"

13. When a 60-degree plumbing fitting is used, the complementary angle is _____.

    A. 30
    B. 60
    C. 120
    D. 300

14. A right triangle has one side measures 6 feet; the other side measures 8 feet, the diagonal is _____ feet.

    A. 9
    B. 10
    C. 11
    D. 12

15. To calculate length, which lies along a 45-degree angle, one would use the decimal value of _____.

    A. 1.144
    B. 1.321
    C. 1.414
    D. 1.732

16. Schedule 40 PVC pipe is rated at 62% of its strength at 100°F compared to its strength at 73.4°F. The maximum water pressure, which may be used at 100°F, is _____ psi.

    A. 45.5
    B. 99.2
    C. 117.4
    D. 160

17. Assume only 5-foot lengths of cast iron pipe are used. Estimate the number of full lengths used in the construction of a pipeline, which measures 162'- 3".

    A. 30
    B. 31
    C. 32
    D. 33

18. Refer to the previous question. Estimate the length of the additional piece required.

    A. 0.45'
    B. 2'- 2 1/2"
    C. 2'- 3"
    D. 4'- 6"

19. Refer to the previous question. The length of the scrap remaining after cutting is _____.

    A. 0.55'
    B. 2'- 71/2"
    C. 2'- 9"
    D. 6.60"

20. An assistant holds a rod on a benchmark of 7.50' and the contractor takes a backsight rod reading of 4.50'. The contractor turns the level and reads the rod, placed on the septic tank inlet, giving a foresight rod reading of 7.25'. The inlet elevation of the septic tank is _____ feet.

    A. Elevation 4.75
    B. Elevation 5.50
    C. Elevation 7.25
    D. Elevation 7.50

21. Which of the septic tank sizes listed below could hold 1,250 gallons in capacity?

    A. 4'- 6" x 5'- 6" x 6'- 6" inside dimension
    B. 4'- 8" x 5'- 4" x 6'- 0" inside dimension
    C. 4'- 8" x 5'- 2" x 6'- 6" inside dimension
    D. 5'- 0" x 5'- 6" x 6'- 2" inside dimension

22. The inside of a single compartment septic tank measures 5'- 4" in width, 5'- 8" in depth, and has a capacity to hold 1,500 gallons. The inside length of the tank would be _____.

    A. 6'- 4"
    B. 6'- 8"
    C. 7'- 0"
    D. 7'- 4"

23. A water tank has a capacity to hold 1,000 gallons. Which of the following is true?

    A. The water in the tank, when full, will weigh approximately 8,330 pounds
    B. The volumetric capacity of the water tank is approximately 133 cubic feet
    C. The volumetric capacity of the water tank is approximately 3,785 liters
    D. All of the above are true

24. The volumetric capacity of a 5-foot diameter half-sphere is _____ gallons.

    A. 32.7
    B. 65.4
    C. 245
    D. 490

25. The total weight of a water filled 21-foot length of 2-inch Schedule 40 steel pipe is _____ pounds.

    A.  30.5
    B.  77.5
    C.  102
    D.  108

26. The total weight of a water filled 10-foot length of 4-inch Schedule 40 steel pipe is _____ pounds.

    A.  55
    B.  109
    C.  164
    D.  235

27. A contractor has several lengths of Schedule 40 steel pipe remaining after completing a project. The contractor lists all remaining lengths to be picked up from the project.

2 - 10' lengths of 2" pipe
7 - 21' lengths of 2" pipe
3 - 10' lengths of 3" pipe
4 - 21' lengths of 3" pipe
12 - 4' lengths of 1" pipe

The weight of the Schedule 40 steel pipe to be picked up from the project is _____ pounds.

    A.  625
    B.  1,570
    C.  2,196
    D.  1,214

28. When multiplying decimeters times decimeters times decimeters, the end result is _____.

    A.  10, 100 or 1,000
    B.  Square decimeters
    C.  Linear decimeters
    D.  Cubic decimeters

29. When cutting threads on standard weight steel pipe, the minimum number of threads to be cut is _____, for 2-inch diameter galvanized pipe.

    A.  10
    B.  11
    C.  11 ½
    D.  12

30. A waste oil tank that is 3'3" in diameter and is 6'4" long, will hold _____ gallons of waste oil. Select the closest answer.

    A. 394
    B. 360
    C. 340
    D. 391

31. A lead roof boot with a 5-inch hole that is 18 inches high and has a flat plate area of 18" x 18" requires _____ square feet of lead to make.

    A. 3.2
    B. 4.1
    C. 8.2
    D. 9.1

32. On a standard weight 2 ½-inch pipe has _____ threads per inch.

    A. 8
    B. 16
    C. 22
    D. 24

33. A run of pipe that is 60 feet long with a grade of ¼-inch fall per foot will drop _____ far.

    A. 7.5
    B. 10
    C. 12
    D. 15

****Please see Answer Key on the following page****

# Mathematics for Plumbers and Pipefitters, 8th Ed.
## Answers

| | Answer | Page # / Solution |
|---|---|---|
| 1. | C | 27 |
| 2. | B | 83 |
| 3. | C | 107 |
| 4. | B | 172 |
| 5. | A | 188 |
| 6. | D | 105 |
| 7. | A | 119 |
| 8. | C | 137 |
| 9. | C | 153 |
| 10. | B | 133 |
| 11. | C | 32-33<br>$13.67' \div 3 = 4.55'$ 4 is feet 4'<br>$.55' \times 12 = 6.60"$ 6 is inches 6"<br>$.60" \times 16 = 9.6$ or $10/16^{th} = 5/8"$ |
| 12. | B | 32-33<br>$21.08' \div 4 = 5.27'$ 5 is feet 5'<br>$.27' \times 12 = 3.24"$ 3 is inches 3"<br>$.24" \times 16 = 3.84$ or $4/16^{th} = 1/4"$ |
| 13. | A | 62 |
| 14. | B | 22 |
| 15. | C | 30 |
| 16. | B | 47<br>160 psi x .62 = 99.2 psi |
| 17. | C | 106<br>$162.25' \div 5' = 32.45 = 32$ full lengths |
| 18. | C | 106<br>.45 x 5' = 2.25' = 2' - 3" additional |
| 19. | C | 106<br>6.55 x 5' = 2.75' = 2'- 9" scrap |
| 20. | A | 233<br>BM + BS = HI - FS = SE<br>7.50' + 4.50' = 12.00' - 7.25' = 4.75' |

|  | **Answer** | **Page # / Solution** |
|---|---|---|

21.    D

172
Convert to cubic feet, $1,250 \div 7.5 = 166.66$ cubic feet

22.    B

33 (#7)
Convert to cubic feet, $1,500 \div 7.5 = 200$ cubic feet
L' x W'
200 cubic feet $\div$ (5.33' x 5.67') = 6.61' length
30.22 sq. ft.
6.61' is 6 feet
.61' x 12 = 7.32" = 7 inches
.32" x 16 = 5.12 = 5/16$^{th}$

23.    D

172 – 173
1,000 gallons x 8.33 pounds per gallons = 8,330 pounds
1,000 gallons $\div$ 7.5 gallons per cubic foot = 133 cubic feet
1,000 gallons x 8.33 pounds $\div$ 2.2 pounds per kilogram = 3,785 kg
Note: 1 liter = 1 kilogram therefore, 3.785 liters = 1 gallon

24.    C

172, 179
0.2618 x 5 x 5 x 5 = 32.7 cubic feet x 7.5 = 245.25

25.    D

230
1.453 + 3.690 = 5.143 x 21 = 108 pounds

26.    C

230
5.512 + 10.9 = 16.412 x 10 = 164 pounds

27.    B

230
2 x 10 x 3.690 = 73.80
7 x 21 x 3.690 = 542.43
3 x 10 x 7.660 = 229.80
4 x 21 x 7.660 = 643.44
12 x 4 x 1.690 = 81.12
1,570.59

28.    D

2
3 dimensional is cubic volume

29.    C

229

30.    A

176
V = .0408 x D" x D" x H"
.0408 x 39 x 39 x 6.33
V = 392.82

31.    B

168
Cylinder = 18 x 3.14 x 5 = 282.6$^{2}$"
Plate = 18 x 18 = 324$^{2}$"
Subtract hole $\pi r^2$
3.14 x 2.5 x 2.5 = 19. 6$^{2}$"
282.6 + 324 – 19.6 = 587$^2$
587 $\div$ 144 = 4.08

|     | **Answer** | **Page # / Solution** |
|-----|------------|----------------------|
| 32. | A          | 261                  |
| 33. | D          | 123                  |

33. $60 \times .25 = 15"$

# OSHA - (29 CFR PART 1926)
# Questions and Answers

1. The ratio of the ultimate breaking strength of a piece of equipment to the actual working stress when in use is known as the _____.

A. occupational hazard        B. construction condition
C. condition of protection       D. safety factor

2. A female employee complains that there are not separate toilets for the 20 women working on the site. She further states that all 160 males and females use the same toilet. She said that the contractor is not complying with OSHA. According to OSHA, the employee_____.

A. does not have a valid complaint since OSHA has no specific instructions as to male and female toilets. The project is only required to have four toilets and four urinals.
B. does not have a valid complaint since OSHA has no specific instructions as to male and female toilets. The project is only required to have five toilets and five urinals.
C. has a valid complaint since OSHA specifies that five toilets and five urinals for men and a separate toilet for women are required on a project of that size.
D. has a valid complaint since OSHA specifies five toilets and four urinals for men and a separate toilet for women are required on a project of that size.

3. A first aid kit must be checked_____ .

A. daily       B. weekly       C. monthly       D. annually

4. Potable drinking water, per OSHA requires:

A. if a container is used it must have a tap.
B. a common drinking cup is allowed if washed.
C. single serving cups do not have to be provided.
D. open containers can be used if single serving cups are provided.

5. One toilet shall be provided at the construction job site for maximum of _____ employees.

A. 5                  B. 10                  C.  15.                  D. 20

6. Given the following:          1-1/2 hr noise exposure at 90 dBA
                                 1/2 hr noise exposure at 100 dBA
                                 1/2 hr noise exposure at 105 dBA
If your employees are exposed to all of the above noise levels each work day, then according to OSHA the "equivalent noise exposure factor":

A. exceeds unity, therefore the noise exposure is within permissible levels
B. exceeds unity, therefore the noise exposure is not within permissible levels
C. Does not exceed unity, therefore the noise exposure is within permissible limits
D. does not exceed unity, therefore the noise exposure is not within permissible limits.

7. Safety nets, where required, shall be provided when workplaces are more than _____ feet above the ground or water surface.

A. 100
B. 75
C. 50
D. 25

8. The Code of Federal Regulations, 1926.1060, requires an employer to provide a training program for each employee:

A. using ladders and stairways
B. working with toxic substances
C. working in excavations
D. using scaffolding

9. According to OSHA, the minimum illumination of indoor corridors during construction is _____ foot candles.

A. 3                  B. 5                  C. 10                  D. 30

10. Regarding personal protection life saving equipment, OD refers to_____.

A. over design                          B. outside perimeter
C. optical density                      D. operating difficulty

1. According to OSHA, life lines used for employee safeguarding shall have a minimum breaking strength of _____ pounds.

A. 500 pounds          B.4000          C.3500          D.5400

12. The maximum distance a man wearing a safety belt may drop or work is:

A. 3 feet　　　　　B. 6 feet　　　　　C. 12 feet　　　　　D. 15 feet

13. When working with scaffolds over water what precaution is required?

A. ever worker must wear safety shoes
B. all personnel should be instructed in life saving
C. all personnel should be wearing a life jacket or floatation, vest
D. scaffolds should not be build over water without safety nets

14. According to OSHA, a fire extinguisher rated not less than 2A shall be provided for each (maximum) of the protected building area.

A. 1500 sq. ft.　　　　　B. 2000 sq. ft.　　　　　C. 2500 sq. ft.　　　　　D. 3000 s

15. A fire breaks out in a main electrical junction box at a construction site, an electrician is lose by and asks you to get a fire extinguisher. According to OSHA, which of the following extinguishers should you bring back?

A. soda acid　　　　　　　　　　B. foam
C. stored pressure (water type)　　　　D. CO2

16. A class A fire consists of burning_____.

A. wood　　　　　　　　　　B. oil
C. electrical equipment　　　　D. metals

17. According to OSHA, material shall not be stored within _____inches from a fire door:

A. 24 inches　　　　　B. 30 inches　　　　　C. 36 inches　　　　　D. 48 inches

18. According to OSHA, no more than _____gallons of flammable or combustible liquids shall be stored in a room outside of an approved storage cabinet.

A. 10 gallons　　　　　B. 15 gallons　　　　　C. 20 gallons　　　　　D. 25 gallons

19. According to OSHA, a sign lettered in legible red letters, not less than 6 inches high on a white field is used only as a/an_____ sign.

A. danger　　　　　B. exit　　　　　C. caution　　　　　D. safety instructional

20. Material stored inside building under construction shall not be placed within _____ of any hoistway opening or inside floor openings.

A. 4'            B. 5'            C. 6'            D. 10'

21. Wire rope shall not be used if in any strength of 8 diameters the total number of visible broken wires exceed _____ % of the total number of wires.

A. 5            B. 10            C. 15            D. 20

22. According to OSHA, scaffolds and their components shall be capable of supporting without failure at least _____ times their maximum intended load.

A. 2            B. 3            C. 4            D. 5

23. Scaffold planks shall extend over end supports not less _____ inches and not more than _____ inches.

A. 6---12            B. 8---12            C. 9---12            D. 10---16

24. A standard toe board shall be a minimum of _____ inches high.

A. 3 inches            B. 3- 1/2 inches            C. 4 inches            D. 4- 1/2 inches

25. According to OSHA, the maximum permissible span for 2 x 10 inch planks used on scaffolding with a working load of 75 psf is _____ feet. Assume full thickness, undressed lumber is used.

A. 10            B. 8            C. 6            D. 4

26. A gap or void 2 inches or more in its least dimension in a floor, roof, or other walking/working surface is a _____.

A. toe hole            B. floor hole            C. breech            D. opening

27. According to OSHA, every open sided floor or platform (other than scaffolding) _____ feet or more above adjacent floor or ground level shall be guarded by a standard railing, or the equivalent, on all open sides, except where there is entrance to a ramp, stairway or fixed ladder.

A. 6 feet            B. 8 feet            C. 10 feet            D. 12 feet

28. The vertical height of a guard rail shall be:

A. 30 inches            B. 36 inches            C. 42 inches            D. 48 inches

29. Where electrical transmission lines are energized and rated at least 50 KV or less, a clearance of _____ feet minimum must be maintained by the crane and load.

A. 5 feet          B. 8 feet          C. 10 feet          D. 12 feet

30. According to OSHA safety and health regulation for construction, the minimum diameter wire ropes used in personnel hoists shall be_____ inch.

A. ½          B. 5/8          C. ¾          D. 7/8

31. When employees are required to be in trenches _____ feet or more in depth, ladders shall be provided for exit, and such ladders shall require not more than _____feet of lateral travel.

A. 4 feet-30 feet                    B. 5 feet- 30 feet
C. 4 feet-25 feet                    D. 5 feet-25 feet

32. According to OSHA, when materials are dropped more than _____ feet outside the exterior walls of a building an enclosed chute must be utilized:

A. 10 feet          B. 15 feet          C. 20 feet          D. 25 feet

33. An electric power circular saw according to OSHA must be:

A. equipped with a constant pressure on switch
B. equipped with a momentary on/off switch that may have a lock on control
C. equipped with a positive on/off control,
D. none of the above

34. For general cleaning operations air pressure must be reduced to less than _____ psi.

A. 15          B. 20          C. 15          D. 30

35. Portable electrical tools do not have to be grounded if_____ .

A. they operate at less than 50 volts
B. equipped with a momentary on/off switch that may have lock on control
C. equipped with a positive on/off control
D. none of the above

36. Referring to power actuated tools, fasteners can be driven into_____.

A. face brick                    B. surface hardened steel
C. cast iron                     D. none of the above

37. According to OSHA, oxygen cylinders, regulators, and hoses shall be:

A. stored only in approved containers
B. prohibited in areas where fuel gasses other than acetylene are used
C. unpainted
D. kept free of all oil or grease

38. Class II hazardous locations are those with a presence of:

A. combustible dust
C. flammable liquids

B. ignitable fibers
D. explosives

39. When employees are required to be in trenches of _____ or more, an adequate means of exit such as a ladder or steps shall be provided.

A. 3 feet
B. 4 feet
C. 5 feet
D. 6 feet

40. In excavations where employees must enter, excavated or other materials may be stored:

A. two feet from the edge of the excavation
B. one foot from the edge of the excavation if properly retained
C. one foot from the edge of the excavation
D. A or B

41. The greatest angle above the horizontal plane for Type A soil is_____ degrees.

A. 34 degrees
B. 45 degrees
C. 53 degrees
D. 90 degrees

42. Sloping or benching for excavation than _____ feet deep shall be designed by a registered professional engineer.

A. 10
B. 15
C. 20
D. 25

43. OSHA requires that for skeleton steel construction no more than _____feet or_____ floors of unfurnished bolting or welding exist:

A. 20 and 2
B. 24 and 2
C. 30 and 3
D. 48 and 4

44. The term "ROPS" means:

A. regional operating standards
B. required operating steps
C. roll over protective structures
D. none of the above

45. According to OSHA, temporary stairs shall have a landing not less than 30" in the direction of travel at every _____(maximum) of vertical rise.

A. 8'             B. 10'             C. 12'             D. 16'

46. Temporary stairs shall be installed at angles to the horizontal of between_____ and_____ degrees.

A. 20 and 40      B. 20 and 50       C. 20 and 30       D. 30 and 50

47. According to OSHA, stairway railings shall be of such construction, to be capable of withstanding a minimum load of _____pounds applied in any direction at any point the top rail.

A. 100            B. 150             C. 200             D. 250

48. Rungs, cleats and steps of portable ladders (except for special applications such as step-stools) shall be spaced not less than _____ inches, nor more than_____ inches.

A.8-11            B.8-14             C. 10-14           D. 12-16

49. The minimum clear distance between the side rails of all portable ladders shall not be less than _____inches.

A. 11 ½           B. 12              C. 13              D. 14

50. A 27 foot ladder that extends the required distance above the landing should have a horizontal distance from the top support to the foot of the ladder of _____feet.

A. 4              B. 5               C. 6               D. 8

# 1 Exam Prep
# OSHA - (29 CFR PART 1926)
# Questions and Answers

## ANSWER KEY

| Answer | Section/Page# |
|---|---|
| 1. D | 1926.32(n) |
| 2. A | Table D-1 |
| 3. B | 1926.50(d)(2) |
| 4. A | 1926.51(a)(2) & (5) |
| 5. D | Table D-1 |
| 6. C | 1926.52, Table D-2 |
| 7. D | 1926.105(a) |
| 8. A | 1926.1060 (a) |
| 9. B | Table D-3 |
| 10. C | 1926.102(b) (24 |
| 11. D | 1926.104(b) |
| 12. B | 1926.104(d) |
| 13. C | 1926.106(a) |
| 14. D | 1926.150(c) |
| 15. D | Table F-1 |
| 16. A | Table F-1 |
| 17. C | 1926.151(d)(7) |
| 18. D | 1926.152(b)(2) |
| 19. B | 1926.200(d) |
| 20. C | 1926.250(b)(1) |
| 21. B | 1926.251(c)(4)(iv) |
| 22. C | 1926.451(a)(1) |
| 23. A | 1926.451(b)(4) & (5) |
| 24. B | 1926.451(h)(4)ii |
| 25. C | Sub. L, App. A |
| 26. B | 1926.500(b) |
| 27. A | 1926.501(b)(2)ii |
| 28. C | 1926.502(b |
| 29. C | 1926.550(a)( |
| 30. A | 1926.552(c)(14)1 |
| 31. C | 1926.651(9)(2) |
| 32. C | 1926.252(a) |
| 33. A | 1926.300(d)(3) |
| 34. D | 1926.302(b)(4) |

35. D   1926.302(a)
36. D   1926.302(e)(7)
37. D   1926.350(i)
38. A   1926.449
39. B   1926.651(c)(2)
40. D   1926.651(j) (2)
41. C   Table B-1.
42. C   Table B-1 note
43. D   1926.750(a)(2)
44. C   1926.1000
45. C   1926.1052(a)(1)
46. D   1926.1052(a)(2)
47. C   1926.1052(c)(5)
48. C   1926.1053(a)(3)
49. A   1926.1053(a)(4)
50. C   1926.1053(b)(1)

# Code of Federal Regulations (OSHA) 29 CFR 1926
# Questions and Answers

1. The minimum distance between side rails for all portable ladders shall not be less than _____ inches.

    A. 11 ½
    B. 12
    C. 14
    D. 16

2. A stairway, ladder, ramp or other safe means of egress shall be located in trench excavations that are _____ feet or more in depth so as to require no more than _____ feet of lateral travel for employees.

    A. 4; 30
    B. 5; 30
    C. 4; 25
    D. 5; 25

3. Stairways that will not be a permanent part of the structure on which construction work is being performed shall have landings of not less than _____ inches in the direction of travel.

    A. 22
    B. 30
    C. 36
    D. 24

4. Toeboards, when used as falling object protection, shall be a minimum of _____ inches in vertical height.

    A. 3 ½
    B. 4
    C. 6
    D. 8

5. Scaffold fabricated planks and platforms shall be designed for a working load of _____ pounds per square foot (psf), if considered light duty.

    A. 15
    B. 20
    C. 25
    D. 50

6. A scaffold designed for 75 pounds per square foot (psf) is classified as _____.

    A. Light-duty
    B. Medium-duty
    C. Heavy-duty
    D. One-person

7. An extra-heavy-duty type 1A metal or plastic ladder shall sustain at least _____ times the maximum intended load.

    A. 2
    B. 2.5
    C. 4
    D. 3.3

8. A bricklayer's square scaffold load shall not exceed _____ pounds per square feet.

    A. 25
    B. 50
    C. 75
    D. 100

9. OSHA requires an employer to provide a training program for each employee _____.

    A. Using ladders and stairways
    B. Working with toxic substances
    C. Working in excavations
    D. Using scaffolding

10. Cord sets and receptacles which are fixed and not exposed to damage shall be tested at intervals not exceeding _____ months.

    A. 2
    B. 3
    C. 4
    D. 6

11. When portable ladders are used for access to an upper landing surface, the ladder side rails shall extend at least _____ feet above the upper landing surface to which the ladder is used to gain access.

    A. 3
    B. 4
    C. 5
    D. 6

12. Personnel hoistway doors or gates shall be not less than _____ high.

    A. 4 feet 6 inches
    B. 6 feet 6 inches
    C. 8 feet 6 inches
    D. None of the above

13. The minimum illumination for indoor corridors during construction shall be _____ foot-candles.

    A. 3
    B. 5
    C. 10
    D. 30

14. The span between hangers for plank-type platforms shall not exceed _____ feet.

    A. 6
    B. 8
    C. 10
    D. 12

15. Bricklayers square scaffolds shall not exceed _____ tiers in height.

    A. 2
    B. 3
    C. 4
    D. 5

16. Where toeboards are used for falling object protection, the toeboard shall be capable of withstanding, without failure, a force of at least _____ pounds applied in any downward or horizontal direction.

    A. 15
    B. 25
    C. 50
    D. 100

17. Fixed ladders without cages or wells shall have a clear width to the nearest permanent object of at least _____ inches on each side of the centerline of the ladder.

    A. 7
    B. 12
    C. 15
    D. 18

18. Rungs, cleats and steps of portable ladders (except for special applications such as stepstools) shall be spaced not less than _____ inches apart, nor more than _____ inches.

    A. 8; 11
    B. 9; 14
    C. 10; 14
    D. 12; 16

19. Wire rope shall not be used for material handling if in any length of _____ diameter(s) the total number of visible broken wires exceeds 10% of the total number of wires.

    A. 12
    B. 18
    C. 10
    D. 8

20. The minimum illumination of general construction area lighting is _____ foot-candles.

    A. 3
    B. 5
    C. 10
    D. 30

21. All new safety nets shall meet accepted performance standards of _____.

    A. 17,500 foot-pounds minimum impact resistance
    B. 24,000 foot-pounds minimum impact resistance
    C. Withstand five 200-pound sacks dropped simultaneously from a height of 25 feet
    D. 10,000-pound rope tensile strength

22. The contents of the first aid kit shall be placed in a weatherproof container with individual sealed packages for each type of item, and shall be checked by the employer before being sent out on each job and at least _____ on each job to ensure that the expended items are replaced.

    A. Daily
    B. Weekly
    C. Monthly
    D. Annually

23. If the personnel hoist wire rope speed is 300 feet per minute, the minimum rope safety factor must be _____.

    A. 9.20
    B. 9.50
    C. 9.75
    D. 10.00

24. The use of non-self-supporting ladders shall be at such an angle that the horizontal distance from the top support to the foot of the ladder is approximately _____ of the working length of the ladder.

    A. One-half
    B. One-quarter
    C. Three quarters
    D. Seven eighths

25. Stairs shall be installed between _____ and _____ degrees horizontal.

    A. 20; 40
    B. 20; 50
    C. 20; 30
    D. 30; 50

26. Each employee on walking/working surfaces shall be protected from falling through holes, including skylights, by covers capable of supporting, without failure _____ that may be imposed on the cover at any one time.

    A. At least twice the weight of employees, equipment and materials
    B. An 800-pound load
    C. A force of at least 200 pounds
    D. A force of at least 150 pounds

27. Class II hazardous locations are those that are hazardous because of the presence of _____.

    A. Combustible dust
    B. Ignitable fibers
    C. Flammable liquids
    D. Explosives

28. Combustible materials shall be piled with regard to the stability of the piles and in no case shall be higher than _____ feet.

    A. 12
    B. 14
    C. 16
    D. 20

29. OSHA requires that for a structural steel assembly, at no time shall there be more than _____ feet or _____ floors, whichever is less, of unfinished bolting or welding above the foundation.

    A. 20; 2
    B. 24; 2
    C. 30; 3
    D. 48; 4

30. The term "ROPS" means _____.

    A. Regional Operating Standards
    B. Required Operating Steps
    C. Rollover Protective Structures
    D. None of the above

31. The maximum allowable slope for Type A soil for a simple slope in an excavation of 20 feet or less in depth is _____.

    A. 1: 1
    B. 2: 1
    C. ½: 1
    D. ¾: 1

32. When employees are required to be in trenches of _____ feet or more, an adequate means of egress such as a ladder, stairway or ramp shall be provided.

    A. 3
    B. 4
    C. 5
    D. 6

33. Openings are defined as a gap or void _____.

    A. 12 inches or less in its least dimension in a floor
    B. 30 inches or more high and 18 inches or more wide in a wall
    C. Less than 12 inches but more than 1 inch in its least dimension in a floor
    D. 12 inches or more in its greatest dimension in a floor

34. The top edge height of top rails, or equivalent guardrail system members, shall be _____ inches.

    A. 30
    B. 36
    C. 42
    D. 48

35. The use of spiral stairways that will not be a permanent part of the structure on which construction work is being performed is _____.

    A. Permitted
    B. Prohibited
    C. Prohibited except with the permission of the building official
    D. Permitted if the stairway is at least 7 feet in diameter

36. One toilet shall be provided at the construction jobsite for a maximum of _____ employees.

    A. 5
    B. 10
    C. 15
    D. 20

37. A Class C fire is a fire caused by _____.

    A. Combustible metal
    B. Flammable liquid
    C. Trash
    D. Electrical equipment

38. When materials are dropped more than _____ feet outside the exterior walls of a building, an enclosed chute shall be used.

    A. 10
    B. 15
    C. 20
    D. 25

39. Material shall not be stored indoors within _____ inches of a fire door opening.

    A. 24
    B. 30
    C. 36
    D. 48

40. Scaffold planking that is nominal two inches thick shall be used for a _____ psf workload at a maximum span of _____ feet.

    A. 25; 10
    B. 50; 8
    C. 75; 6
    D. 25; 8

41. OSHA requires that a safety factor based on load and speed be used in hoist cables. The safety factor for a cable with a speed of 200 feet per minute is _____.

    A. 7.00
    B. 6.65
    C. 7.65
    D. 8.60

42. Safety belt lanyards used for employee safeguarding shall have a minimum breaking strength of _____ pounds.

    A. 1,000
    B. 4,000
    C. 5,000
    D. 5,400

43. The proper maintenance for a carbon dioxide type fire extinguisher is to _____.

    A. Discharge annually and recharge
    B. Check pressure gauge monthly
    C. Check pressure gauge annually
    D. Weigh semi-annually

44. No more than _____ gallons of flammable or combustible liquids shall be stored in a room outside of an approved storage cabinet.

    A. 10
    B. 15
    C. 20
    D. 25

45. Exposure to impulsive or impact noise shall not exceed _____ dBA peak sound pressure level.

    A. 92
    B. 110
    C. 140
    D. 188

46. Simple slope-short-term excavations in Type A soil with a maximum depth of 12 feet shall have a maximum allowable slope of _____.

    A. 1: 1
    B. 2: 1
    C. ¾: 1
    D. ½: 1

47. The ratio of the ultimate breaking strength of a piece of material or equipment to the actual working stress when in use is known as the _____.

    A. Occupational hazard
    B. Unstructibility
    C. Condition of protection
    D. Safety factor

48. Wire, synthetic or fiber rope used for scaffold suspension shall be capable of supporting at least _____ times the rated load.

    A. 6
    B. 4
    C. 3
    D. 2

49. The proper maintenance for a multi-purpose ABC dry chemical stored pressure fire extinguisher is to _____.

    A. Check pressure gauge monthly
    B. Discharge annually and recharge
    C. Weigh semi-annually
    D. Check pressure gauge and condition of dry chemical annually

50. Metal tubular frame scaffolds, including components such as braces, brackets, trusses, screws legs, ladders, etc. shall be designed, constructed and erected to safely support its own weight and at least _____ times the maximum intended load applied.

    A. 6
    B. 2
    C. 3
    D. 4

51. The maximum span of 2" x 10" undressed lumber on a scaffold when loaded with 50 psf shall be _____ feet.

    A. 5
    B. 6
    C. 10
    D. 8

52. On construction sites, a fire extinguisher rated not less than 2A shall be provided for each _____ square feet of the protected building area, or major fraction thereof.

    A. 1,000
    B. 2,000
    C. 3,000
    D. 4,000

53. Potable drinking water, per OSHA, requires that _____.

    A. If a container is used it shall be equipped with a tap
    B. A common drinking cup is allowed if washed
    C. Single serving cups do not have to be provided
    D. Open containers can be used if single serving cups are provided

54. A safety belt lanyard shall provide for a fall not greater than _____ feet.

    A. 3
    B. 6
    C. 12
    D. 15

55. The maximum allowable height of a horse scaffold shall be two tiers or _____ feet.

    A. 4
    B. 8
    C. 12
    D. 10

56. When using carpenters' bracket scaffolds, the _____.

    A. Brackets shall be spaced a maximum of 8 feet
    B. Bolts used to attach shall be not less than 5/8 inches in diameter
    C. Tools and materials shall not exceed 75 pounds
    D. All of the above

57. When a material hoist tower is not enclosed, the hoist platform shall _____.

    A. Be caged on all sides
    B. Have ½-inch mesh number 16 U.S. gage wire covering
    C. Have a five-foot enclosure at ground level
    D. All of the above

58. Employees cannot be subjected to noise levels higher than _____ dBA for more than four hours per day.

    A. 95
    B. 97
    C. 102
    D. 105

59. The range of maximum intended working loads for light to heavy-duty Independent Wood Pole Scaffolds shall be _____ pounds per square foot (psf).

    A. 20 – 75
    B. 25 – 70
    C. 25 – 75
    D. 25 – 50

60. Safety nets shall be provided when workplaces are more than _____ feet above the ground or water surface.

    A. 6
    B. 8
    C. 10
    D. 25

61. No more than _____ employee(s) shall occupy any given eight feet of a form scaffold at any one time.

    A. 1
    B. 2
    C. 3
    D. 4

62. Given the following: 1 ½ hours noise exposure at 90 dBA
  ½ hour noise exposure at 100 dBA
  ¼ hour noise exposure at 110 dBA

If your employees are exposed to all of the above noise levels each workday, the "Equivalent Noise Exposure Factor _____.

  A. Exceeds unity, therefore the noise exposure is within permissible levels
  B. Exceeds unity, therefore the noise exposure is not within permissible levels
  C. Does not exceed unity, therefore the noise exposure is within permissible limits
  D. Does not exceed unity, therefore the noise exposure is not within permissible limits

63. A fire breaks out in a main electrical junction box at a construction site, an electrician is close by and asks you to get a fire extinguisher. According to OSHA, you should bring back a _____ extinguisher.

  A. Soda acid
  B. Foam
  C. Stored pressure (water type)
  D. CO$_2$

64. Oxygen cylinders, regulators and hoses shall be _____.

  A. Stored only in approved containers
  B. Prohibited in areas where fuel gasses other than acetylene are used
  C. Unpainted
  D. Kept away from oil or grease

65. A female employee complains that there are not separate toilets for the 20 women working on the site. She further states that all 160 employees use the same toilet. She said that the contractor is not complying with OSHA. According to the text, the employee _____.

  A. Does not have a valid complaint since OSHA has no specific instructions as to male and female toilets. The project is only required to have four toilets and four urinals
  B. Does not have a valid complaint since OSHA has no specific instructions as to male and female toilets. The project is only required to have five toilets and five urinals
  C. Has a valid complaint since OSHA specifies that five toilets and five urinals for men and a separate toilet for women are required on a project of that size
  D. Has a valid complaint since OSHA specifics four toilets and four urinals for men and a separate toilet for women are required on a project of that size

66. Employees shall not be exposed to noise levels exceeding _____ dBA for more than eight hours a day.

  A. 90
  B. 95
  C. 102
  D. 105

67. A Class A fire consists of burning _____.

    A. Wood
    B. Oil
    C. Electrical equipment
    D. Metals

68. Portable electric lighting used in wet and/or other conductive locations shall be operated at _____ volts or less.

    A. 12
    B. 32
    C. 110
    D. 220

69. _____ shall not be used if the rope shows other signs of excessive wear, corrosion, or defect.

    A. Alloy steel chains
    B. Synthetic fiber rope
    C. Natural rope
    D. Wire rope

70. According to OSHA, a sign lettered in legible red letters, not less than 6 inches high on a white field is used only as a/an _____ sign.

    A. Danger
    B. Exit
    C. Caution
    D. Safety Instructional

71. Material stored inside building under construction shall not be placed within _____ feet of any hoistway opening or inside floor openings.

    A. 4
    B. 5
    C. 6
    D. 10

72. Scaffold planks shall extend over the centerline of its supports at least _____ inches and not more than _____ inches.

    A. 6; 12
    B. 8; 12
    C. 9; 12
    D. 10; 16

73. A gap or void 2 inches or more in its least dimension in a floor, roof, or other walking/working surface is a _____.

    A. Toeboard
    B. Hole
    C. Breech
    D. Opening

74. Safety and health regulation for construction, the minimum diameter wire ropes used in personnel hoists shall be _____ inch.

    A. ½
    B. 5/8
    C. ¾
    D. 7/8

75. An electric power circular saw shall be _____.

    A. Equipped with constant pressure switch
    B. Equipped with a momentary on/off switch that may have a lock on control
    C. Equipped with a positive on/off control
    D. None of the above

76. For general cleaning operations, the compressed air shall be reduced to less than _____ psi.

    A. 100
    B. 20
    C. 25
    D. 30

77. For powder-actuated tools, fasteners shall be allowed to be driven into _____.

    A. Face brick
    B. Surface-hardened steel
    C. Cast iron
    D. None of the above

78. Sloping or benching for excavation more than _____ feet deep shall be designed by a registered professional engineer.

    A. 10
    B. 15
    C. 20
    D. 25

79. Stairway railings shall be capable of withstanding a minimum force of _____ pounds applied in any downward or outward direction at any point along the top edge.

    A. 100
    B. 150
    C. 200
    D. 250

80. Forms and shores in concrete shall not be removed until _____.

    A. Directed by the architect or engineer
    B. The removal time stated in the specifications has elapsed
    C. The concrete has attained the specified compressive strength
    D. The concrete has gained sufficient strength to support its weight and superimposed loads

81. When ropes are used to define controlled access zones, the rope shall have a minimum breaking strength of _____ pounds.

    A. 75
    B. 100
    C. 200
    D. 300

82. Excavations 8' or less in depth in Type A soil that have unsupported, vertically sided lower portions, shall have a maximum vertical side of _____ feet.

    A. 3
    B. 3.5
    C. 4
    D. 5

83. All the following are true concerning OSHA regulations about employees working over or near water except _____.

    A. Ring buoys with at least 90 feet of line shall be provided and readily available
    B. At least one lifesaving skiff shall be immediately available
    C. Where the danger of drowning exists, provide employees with life jackets or buoyant work vests
    D. At least one person certified in lifesaving swimming courses shall be employed at all times

84. _____ shall be located and determined prior to opening an excavation.

    A. Dump site
    B. Site entrances
    C. Underground installations
    D. Adjacent property elevations

85. The maximum intended load for a frame scaffold including its components is 1,000 pounds. The scaffold as described shall be designed to support a minimum of _____ ton(s).

    A. 1.0
    B. 1.5
    C. 2.0
    D. 4.0

86. Storing masonry blocks in stacks higher than 6 feet shall be permissible provided that _____.

    A. Bracing is installed at the 6-foot level
    B. Containment is provided every 4-foot
    C. The stack is tapered back one-half block per tier above the 6-foot level
    D. The stack is on a concrete floor

87. When hazardous waste cleanup and removal operations at any site take longer than _____ months to complete, the employer shall provide showers and changing rooms for employees exposed to such conditions.

    A. 3
    B. 6
    C. 9
    D. 12

88. No employee shall be exposed to lead at concentrations greater than _____ micrograms per cubic meter of air in an 8-hour period.

    A. 30
    B. 40
    C. 50
    D. 60

89. Training for Class II asbestos removal work requires hands-on training and shall take at least _____ hours.

    A. 2
    B. 8
    C. 12
    D. 16

90. Where oxygen deficiency (atmospheres containing less than 19.5 percent oxygen) or a hazardous atmosphere exists or could reasonably be expected to exist, such as in excavations in landfill areas or excavations in areas where hazardous substances are stored nearby, excavations deeper than _____ feet shall be tested before employees are allowed enter the excavation site.

    A. 3
    B. 4
    C. 5
    D. 6

91. Whenever a masonry wall is being constructed, a limited access zone shall be established. The access zone shall run the entire length of the wall, on the side of the wall that is not scaffolded and extend to the height of the wall to be _____.

    A. Reconstructed
    B. Reconstructed plus two feet
    C. Reconstructed plus four feet
    D. Reconstructed plus six feet

92. An employer shall ensure that no employee is exposed to an airborne concentration of asbestos in excess of _____ fiber(s) per cubic centimeter of air as averaged over a 30-minute sampling period.

    A. 1.0
    B. 2.0
    C. 10.0
    D. 20.0

93. A wire core manila rope is used as a lifeline where it may be subjected to cutting or abrasion. The required minimum size of the rope shall be _____ inch.

    A. 1/2
    B. 3/4
    C. 7/8
    D. 1

94. Routine inspection of open excavations shall be conducted by a competent person _____.

    A. Daily
    B. Weekly
    C. Every two days
    D. Every three days

95. Haulage vehicles, whose payload is loaded by means of cranes, power shovels, loaders, or similar equipment, shall have _____.

    A. Pneumatic tires capable of supporting 1-1/2 times the payload capacity
    B. Automatic dumping mechanisms capable of payload leveling
    C. An automatic transmission and a cab shield on the load side of the operator station
    D. A cab shield and/or canopy adequate to protect the operator from shifting or falling materials

96. When removing hazardous waste materials, personal protection equipment is divided into four categories based upon protection required. _____ has the highest level of respiratory protection but a lesser level of skin protection.

    A. Level A
    B. Level B
    C. Level C
    D. Level D

97. Fuel gas and oxygen manifolds shall NOT be placed _____.

    A. Indirect sunlight
    B. No closer than 15' of main electric
    C. Elevated at least 6' off of a dirt floor
    D. They shall not be located within enclosed areas

98. The term "point of operation" refers to the _____.

    A. Starting point of a project
    B. Specific operation of a project being performed
    C. Area of a project where work is underway
    D. Area on a machine where work is actually performed\

99. For excavation made in Type C soil, the minimum, above the top of the vertical side, that the support shield systems at the vertically sided lower portion of an excavation be shielded or supported shall be _____ inches.

    A. 20
    B. 18
    C. 16
    D. 14

100. The highest stack allowed when bricks are being stored shall be _____ feet.

    A. 5
    B. 7
    C. 9
    D. 10

101. Employees shall be provided with anti-laser eye protection devices when working in areas in which a potential exposure to reflected laser light is greater than _____ milliwatts.

    A. 5
    B. 4
    C. 3
    D. 2

102. The minimum illumination required for first aid stations shall be _____ foot-candles.

    A. 30
    B. 20
    C. 5
    D. 3

103. A job site having 90 employees with temporary restrooms shall have a minimum of _____ toilets and urinals.

    A. One toilet and one urinal
    B. Two toilets and two urinals
    C. Three toilets and three urinals
    D. Four toilets and four urinals

104. Employees shall be protected from excavated or other materials or equipment that could pose a hazard by falling or rolling into excavations. The minimum distance required from the edge of excavations for placing and keeping such materials or equipment is _____ feet.

    A. 2
    B. 3
    C. 4
    D. 5

105. Not more than _____ gallons of Category 4 flammable liquids shall be stored in any one storage cabinet.

    A. 25
    B. 60
    C. 80
    D. 120

106. A hand-held grinder with a 2-1/8" diameter wheel shall be equipped with only a _____.

    A. Constant pressure switch
    B. Momentary contact on/off switch
    C. Positive percussion switch
    D. Positive on/off switch

107. Each end of a scaffold platform, unless cleated or otherwise restrained, shall extend over the centerline of its support at least _____ inches.

    A. 2
    B. 4
    C. 6
    D. 12

108. Where scaffold platforms are overlapped to create a long platform, platforms shall be secured from movement or overlapped at least _____ inches unless the platforms are nailed together or otherwise restrained to prevent movement.

    A. 2
    B. 4
    C. 6
    D. 12

109. When lifting concrete slabs, operation of jacks shall be synchronized in such a manner as to insure even and uniform lifting of the slab. All points of the slab support shall be kept level within _____ inches.

    A. 1/2
    B. 1
    C. 1-1/2
    D. 2

110. A "Controlled Access Zone" is implemented to protect employees from access to an area where the erection of precast concrete members is being performed. The control lines in a "Controlled Access Zone" shall be erected not more than _____ feet from the unprotected or leading edge or half of the length of the member being erected, whichever is less.

    A. 6
    B. 15
    C. 25
    D. 60

111. Shoring for concrete shall be designed by a _____.

    A. Contractor
    B. Carpenter
    C. Qualified designer
    D. Lumber supplier

112. All masonry walls over _____ feet in height shall be adequately braced to prevent overturning and to prevent collapse unless the wall is adequately supported so that it will not overturn or collapse.

    A. 8
    B. 12
    C. 16
    D. 20

113. Self-supporting portable ladders shall be capable of supporting without failure at least _____ times the maximum intended load.

    A. 3
    B. 4
    C. 5
    D. 6

114. A non-self-supporting ladder has a working length of 20'. According to OSHA, the horizontal distance from the top support to the foot of the ladder is approximately _____ foot/feet.

    A. 1/4 of a
    B. 4
    C. 5
    D. 6

115. During asbestos removal, the asbestos disposal contractor shall erect _____ rooms in the decontamination area.

    A. 2
    B. 3
    C. 4
    D. 5

116. All pneumatic nailers, staplers and other similar equipment provided with automatic fastener feed shall have a safety device to prevent the tool from ejecting fasteners when operation pressures exceed _____ psi.

    A. 75
    B. 100
    C. 125
    D. 150

117. A portable ladder that is NOT self-supporting must be capable of supports at least _____ times the maximum intended load.

    A. 2
    B. 4
    C. 6
    D. 8

118. The common drinking cup is _____.

    A. Prohibited
    B. Not prohibited
    C. Prohibited in areas where more than 3 workmen will use the cup
    D. Prohibited in hazardous areas

119. Eye protection near dangerous working conditions _____.

    A. Is required at the employee's cost
    B. Is required at the employer's cost
    C. Can only be required by union regulations
    D. Is not required

120. During construction, the minimum illumination required for an indoor warehouse shall be _____ foot- candles.

    A. 3
    B. 5
    C. 10
    D. 30

121. When safety nets are required to be provided, such nets shall extend _____ feet beyond the edge of the work's surface.

    A. 4
    B. 6
    C. 8
    D. 10

122. The mesh size of safety nets shall not exceed _____.

    A. 12" x 12"
    B. 10" x 10"
    C. 8" x 8"
    D. 6" x 6"

123. When masonry blocks are stacked higher than _____ feet, the stack shall be tapered back one-half block per tier above the six-foot level.

    A. 4
    B. 6
    C. 8
    D. 10

124. Lumber that is handled manually shall not be stacked more than _____ feet high.

    A. 14
    B. 16
    C. 18
    D. 20

125. The components of a scaffold loaded with 500 pounds shall be capable of supporting its own weight and a load of at least _____ ton(s) without failure.

    A. 1
    B. 2
    C. 2.5
    D. 4

126. All site clearing equipment shall be equipped with an overhead and rear canopy guard of at least 1/8" steel plate or _____ inch woven wire mesh with openings no greater than one inch, or equivalent.

    A. 1/8
    B. 1/4
    C. 3/8
    D. 1/2

127. Where doors or gates open directly on a stairway, a platform shall be provided, and the swing of the door shall not reduce the effective width of the platform to less than _____ inches.

    A. 16
    B. 18
    C. 20
    D. 24

128. Cohesive soil packed with an unconfined compressive strength of less than 1.5 tons per square foot but greater than .5 tons per square foot is defined as _____.

    A. Type A
    B. Type B
    C. Type C
    D. Type D

129. A six-foot deep trench excavated in Type C soil shall have the sides sloped at a maximum of _____.

    A. ¾:1
    B. 1:1
    C. 1 ½ : 1
    D. 1 ½: 1 ½

130. A simple slope excavation with a depth of 10 feet and which will be open for 20 hours shall have a maximum allowable slope of _____ in Type A soil.

    A. 1: ¾
    B. ¾ : 1
    C. 1: ½
    D. ½ : 1

131. When Type C soil is excavated over Type A soil, Type A soil shall be excavated to a maximum slope of _____ in layered soils.

    A. 1: ¾
    B. 1:1
    C. ¾ : 1
    D. 1 ½ : 1

132. Lifting inserts that are embedded, or otherwise attached to precast concrete members, other than the tilt-up members, shall be capable of supporting at least _____ times the intended maximum load.

    A. 2
    B. 3
    C. 4
    D. 5

133. The maximum number of manually controlled jacks allowed for lift-slab construction operations shall be limited to _____ on one slab.

    A. 8
    B. 10
    C. 12
    D. 14

134. The approximate angle of repose for sloping the sides of an excavation, less than 20' deep, in sand shall be _____.

    A. 90°
    B. 53°
    C. 45°
    D. 34°

135. When excavating in the proximity of adjoining buildings, a general contractor shall _____ for the safety and protection of workers.

    A. Remove all loose soils and rocks
    B. Compact adjacent soils and slope walls
    C. Provide adequate shoring and bracing systems
    D. Request a variance to move excavation farther away

136. When single post shores are tiered, they shall _____.

    A. Never be spliced
    B. Be vertically aligned
    C. Be designed by a licensed engineer
    D. Be adequately braced at top and bottom

137. When erecting systems-engineered metal buildings, during placing of rigid frame members, the load is not to be released from the hoisting equipment until _____.

    A. The crane operator signals that is safe to proceed
    B. All bolts have been installed and tightened to the specified torque
    C. The members are secured with not less than 50% of the required bolts at each connection
    D. Drift pins have driven into at least two bolt holes at each connection for the member

138. Prior to site layout, the contractor shall _____.

    A. Obtain a certificate of occupancy and provide proof of occupancy
    B. Alert subcontractors to the requirements of their scope
    C. Start erecting structural steel and roof support members
    D. Locate surface encumbrances that may pose a hazard to employees

139. Drawings or plans, including all revisions, for concrete formwork (including shoring equipment) shall be available at the _____.

    A. Jobsite
    B. Owner's office
    C. Contractor's main office
    D. Building department's office

140. Shoring for supported concrete slabs shall be removed only when the contractor _____.

    A. Has had it inspected by the building inspector
    B. Makes sure the concrete is dry to the touch
    C. Determines that the concrete has gained sufficient strength to support its weight and superimposed loads
    D. Has been told by the concrete supervisor that it is safe to strip the shoring

141. Where electrical transmission lines are energized and rated at least 50 kW or less, a minimum clearance distance of _____ feet shall be maintained.

    A. 5
    B. 8
    C. 10
    D. 12

142. When debris is dropped through a hole in the floor without the use of chute, the drop area shall be enclosed with barricades measuring a minimum of _____ inches.

    A. 30
    B. 36
    C. 42
    D. 48

143. _____ require "point of operation guarding."

    A. Hand chisels
    B. Guillotine cutters
    C. Powder-actuated tools
    D. 1 ½ inch abrasive wheel grinder

144. A _____ scaffold has an adjustable platform mounted on an independent support frame and is equipped with a means to permit platform raising or lowering.

    A. Multi-point adjustable suspension
    B. Single-point adjustable suspension
    C. Two-point adjustable suspension
    D. Masons' adjustable supported

145. At more than _____ feet above a lower level, the tubular welded frame scaffolding shall have approved guardrails and toe boards at all open sides and ends.

    A. 4
    B. 6
    C. 10
    D. 12

146. A minimum of _____ bolts shall be in place at each structural steel beam connection during final placing of solid web members before the load is released.

    A. One
    B. Two
    C. Three
    D. Four

147. The maximum allowable height, without being retrained from tipping, for a free-standing mobile scaffold tower that has a base width of 4 feet is _____ feet.

    A. 12
    B. 16
    C. 20
    D. 24

148. The minimum plywood thickness required for an overhead protective covering above a material or personnel hoist cage is _____ inch(es).

    A. 5/8
    B. ¾
    C. 7/8
    D. ½

149. The maximum permissible span for a 2" x 9" full thickness undressed lumber scaffold plank, when used for a light duty rated load is _____ feet.

    A. 6
    B. 8
    C. 9
    D. 10

150. The maximum intended load on a float or ship scaffold shall be _____ lbs.

    A. 250
    B. 500
    C. 750
    D. 1,000

151. Which of the following is true about electric power-operated tools furnished by the contractor,

      A. Each tool shall be cleaned daily after use
      B. Each tool shall be checked daily before use
      C. Each tool shall be tested daily before use
      D. Each tool shall be double insulated or grounded

152. A _____ is an accidental failure of a cross brace in an excavation.

      A. Kickout
      B. Slip-in
      C. Workout
      D. Cave-in

153. The maximum permissible span for 1 ¼ x 9-inch full thickness wood plank having a maximum intended load of 50 pounds per square foot is _____ feet.

      A. 4
      B. 6
      C. 8
      D. 10

154. The minimum breaking strength for vertical lifelines used for fall protection shall be _____ pounds.

      A. 3,000
      B. 4,000
      C. 5,000
      D. 5,400

155. _____ gauge U.S. standard wire is used for the screen between the toe boards and top rails of an approved guardrail system.

      A. No. 12
      B. No. 14
      C. No. 16
      D. No. 18

156. A ground fault circuit interrupter, GFCI, which is not a part of the permanent wiring of the building on a construction site, protects the _____.

      A. Cord sets
      B. Power tools
      C. Personnel
      D. Wiring

157. The maximum opening size permitted in the ¼" woven wire mesh, used as a rear canopy guard on rider-operated equipment, when used for site clearing shall be _____ inch.

    A. 1
    B. ¾
    C. ½
    D. ¼

158. When a contractor discovers a piece of machinery on site which is not in compliance with OSHA requirements the contractor should _____.

    A. Physically remove the machinery from the site
    B. Identify the problem and inform anyone who operates it
    C. Only operate the machinery on weekend or holidays
    D. Schedule service to remedy the problem within 48 hours

159. A general contractor is building an apartment building with two exterior balconies. The general contractor and the carpentry subcontractor sign an agreement where the carpentry subcontractors will provide all temporary railings. There are 3 other subcontractors and their employees working on the site, using the balconies, when an OSHA inspector arrived and found the railing to be inadequate and unsafe. Which of the following represents the most likely outcome of this inspection visit?

    A. The general contractor and all subcontractors on site will be fined the full amount
    B. Only the carpentry subcontractor will be fined the full amount
    C. Only the general contractor can be fined on the project
    D. Only the general and the carpentry subcontractor will be fined

160. Of the following, which is not a true statement per OSHA regulations?

    A. Jobsite first-aid kits shall be checked by the employer daily
    B. Common drinking cups are prohibited for potable water
    C. A jobsite with 50 employees must have 2 toilets and 2 urinals
    D. The maximum duration of exposure to a sound level of 92 dba is 6 hours

161. According to OSHA, a hazardous atmosphere containing less than _____ percent oxygen may exist in deep excavations.

    A. 100
    B. 75
    C. 50
    D. 19.5

162. Which of the following is a true statement concerning OSHA regulations?

    A. Manually stacked lumber piles shall not be more than 16 feet in height
    B. Material stored inside building may not be placed within 2 feet of doors
    C. Brick stacks shall not be more than 6 feet in height
    D. Masonry blocks shall not be stacked more than 7 feet in height

163. Employers shall not issue or permit the use of unsafe hand tools. Which of the following tools is considered unsafe?

    A. A drift pin with a mushroomed head
    B. A splintered wooden handled shovel
    C. A pipe wrench with a sprung jaw
    D. All of the above are unsafe tools

164. Powder-actuated tools shall be tested _____ to insure proper working condition.

    A. Every hour of each day in use
    B. Each day before loading
    C. One per week
    D. After a malfunction occurs

165. "Asbestos containing material" is any material that contains _____ asbestos.

    A. Up to one percent
    B. More than one percent
    C. Two percent or less
    D. Between five and seven percent

166. Guarding for use with belts, gears, shafts, pulleys, drums, fly wheels or other power operated tools with reciprocating, rotating or moving parts should meet the requirements of _____.

    A. OSHA Regulations
    B. American National Standards Institute
    C. Florida Building Code
    D. U.S. Department of Labor

167. In excavations where a trench shield system is installed, the maximum depth of earth material that can be excavated below the bottom of the shield is _____ inches.

    A. Zero
    B. Not more than 6
    C. Not more than 12
    D. Not more than 24

168. In accordance with OSHA, the _____ has the responsibility of being safe, conducting activities safely and in accordance with all applicable laws and rules.

    A. Individual
    B. Employer
    C. Building official
    D. Foreman

169. The minimum number of sanitation facilities (chemical toilets) required for a 10-person mobile crew having transportation readily available to nearby toilet facilities is _____.

    A. Not less than 1 toilet
    B. 2
    C. 3
    D. Zero

170. _____ soil, which looks and feels damp, can easily be shaped into a ball and rolled into small diameter threads before crumbling.

    A. Cohesive
    B. Fissured
    C. Moist
    D. Granular

171. Inspections of alloy steel chains when used for rigging equipment for material handling shall occur _____.

    A. Daily
    B. Weekly
    C. Monthly
    D. Annually

172. Concrete mixers with _____ or larger loading skips shall be equipped with guardrails installed on each side of the skip.

    A. One cubic foot
    B. Ten cubic feet
    C. One cubic yard
    D. Ten cubic yards

173. A dry chemical, sodium or potassium bicarbonate-based fire extinguisher operated by cartridge is ranked as a type _____ extinguisher.

    A. A
    B. B
    C. C
    D. B and C only

174. When using control lines to demarcate controlled decking zones, non-mandatory guidelines require that each line be rigged and supported in such a way that its highest point is not more than _____ inches from the working surface.

    A. 39
    B. 40
    C. 42
    D. 45

175. A powder-operated tool shall be tested _____.

    A. Each day before loading
    B. Once a week
    C. Once a month
    D. At least semi-annually

176. A room used for storage of more than 60 gallons of flammable or combustible liquids shall have at least one portable fire extinguisher, having a rating of not less than 20-B units, shall be located outside of, but nor more than _____ feet from the door opening into the room.

    A. 5
    B. 7
    C. 10
    D. 12

177. The maximum number of people that can use a ladder jack scaffold at the same time is _____.

    A. 1
    B. 2
    C. 3
    D. 4

178. Guardrail systems shall be designed capable of withstanding a force of at least _____ pounds.

    A. 100
    B. 150
    C. 200
    D. 250

179. Toeboards are required on scaffolding more than _____ feet in height.

    A. 6
    B. 8
    C. 10
    D. 3

180. All pneumatically driven nailers provided with automatic fastener feed, which operate at more than 100 psi pressure at the tool shall have a _____.

    A. Slight angle to the decking
    B. Safety device installed at the muzzle
    C. Regulated pressure to not exceed 110 psi
    D. Regulated pressure not to have less than 90 psi

181. When using a hand-tool that is not grounded, the user should make sure the tool is _____.

    A. Double insulated
    B. Dust free
    C. Newly painted
    D. Serviced by a three-prong adapter

182. Each employee on a scaffold more than _____ feet above a lower level must be protected from falling to that lower level.

    A. 6
    B. 8
    C. 10
    D. 12

183. Scaffolding cannot be moved with employees still on it unless the surface on which it is moving is within _____ degrees of level.

    A. 2
    B. 3
    C. 4
    D. 5

184. Material chutes at an angle of more than 45° from the horizontal shall have openings not to exceed _____ inches in height.

    A. 24
    B. 48
    C. 60
    D. 72

185. When it is not practical to use nails to secure roof bracket scaffolds, brackets shall be secured in place with first-grade manila rope of at least _____ inch(es).

    A. ½
    B. ¾
    C. 1
    D. 1 ½

186. The warning line erected around all sides of the roof work area shall not be less than _____ feet from the roof edge when mechanical equipment is not being used.

    A. 3
    B. 4
    C. 5
    D. 6

187. On low-sloped roofs of _____ feet or less in width, the use of a safety monitoring system alone as a means of providing fall protection during roofing operation is permitted.

    A. 40
    B. 45
    C. 50
    D. 60

*** *Please see Answer Key on the following page* ***

# OSHA Federal Safety and Health Regulations
## Questions and Answers
## Answer Key

| Q | Answer | Section # |
|-----|--------|-----------|
| 1. | A | 1926.1053 (a)(4)(ii) |
| 2. | C | 1926.651 (c)(2) |
| 3. | B | 1926.1052 (a)(1) |
| 4. | A | 1926.502 (j)(3) |
| 5. | C | Subpart L, Appendix A 1(c) |
| 6. | C | Subpart L, Appendix A 1(c) |
| 7. | D | 1926.1053 (a)(1)(i) |
| 8. | B | Subpart L, Appendix A 2(e) |
| 9. | A | 1926.1060 (a) |
| 10. | D | 1926.404 (b)(1)(iii)(E)(4) |
| 11. | A | 1926.1053 (b)(1) |
| 12. | B | 1926.552 (c)(4) |
| 13. | B | 1926.56, Table D-3 |
| 14. | C | Subpart L, Appendix A 2(p)(4) |
| 15. | B | 1926.452 (e)(4) |
| 16. | C | 1926.451(h)(4)(i) |
| 17. | C | 1926.1053 (a)(17) |
| 18. | C | 1926.1053 (a)(3)(i) |
| 19. | D | 1926.251 (c)(4)(iv) |
| 20. | B | 1926.56, Table D-3 |
| 21. | A | 1926.105 (d) |
| 22. | B | 1926.50 (d)(2) |
| 23. | A | 1926.552 (c)(14)(iii) |
| 24. | B | 1926.1053 (b)(5)(i) |
| 25. | D | 1926.1052 (a)(2) |
| 26. | A | 1926.501 (b)(4)(ii) & 1926.502(i)(2) |
| 27. | A | 1926.449 |
| 28. | D | 1926.151 (c)(1) |

| Q | Answer | Section # |
|---|---|---|
| 29. | D | 1926.754 (b)(2) |
| 30. | C | 1926.1002 |
| 31. | D | Subpart P, Appendix B, Table B-1 Maximum Allowable Slopes |
| 32. | B | 1926.651 (c)(2) |
| 33. | B | See "Opening" in Glossary or 1926.500(b) |
| 34. | C | 1926.502 (b)(1) |
| 35. | B | 1926.1051 (a)(1) |
| 36. | D | 1926.51, Table D-1 |
| 37. | D | Subpart F, Table F-1 – Fire Extinguishers Data |
| 38. | C | 1926.252 (a) |
| 39. | C | 1926.151 (d)(7) |
| 40. | D | Subpart L, Appendix A, Scaffold Specifications, (1)(b)(i), Table |
| 41. | D | 1926.552 (c)(14)(iii) |
| 42. | D | 1926.104 (d) |
| 43. | D | Subpart F, Table F-1 – Fire Extinguishers Data |
| 44. | D | 1926.152 (b)(1) |
| 45. | C | 1926.52 (e) |
| 46. | D | Subpart P, Appendix B, Table B-1 Maximum Allowable Slopes<br>Figure B-1 Slope Configurations<br>Figure B-1.1 Excavations made in Type A Soil |
| 47. | D | See "Safety Factor" in Glossary or 1926.32(n) |
| 48. | A | 1926.451 (a)(4) |
| 49. | D | Subpart F, Table F-1 – Fire Extinguishers Data |
| 50. | D | 1926.451 (a)(1) |
| 51. | D | Subpart L, Appendix A (1)(b)(i), Table |
| 52. | C | 1926.150 (c)(1)(i) |
| 53. | A | 1926.51 (a)(2) |
| 54. | B | 1926.104 (d) |
| 55. | D | 1926.452 (f)(1) |
| 56. | D | Subpart L, Appendix A, Scaffold Specifications, Paragraph (g)(2)(3)(4) |
| 57. | A | 1926.552 (b)(5)(ii) |
| 58. | A | 1926.52, Table D-2 |

| Q | Answer | Section # |
|---|---|---|
| 59. | C | Subpart L, Appendix A, Scaffold Specifications, 2. Specifications and Tables, (a) Pole Scaffolds, Table: Independent Wood Pole Scaffolds |
| 60. | D | 1926.105 (a) |
| 61. | B | Subpart L, Appendix A, Scaffold Specifications, 2.Specific Guidelines and Tables (g)(4) |
| 62. | C | 1926.52 (d)(2)(iii) $Fe = (T1 \div L1) + (T2 \div L2) + (Tn \div Ln)$ $Fe = (1/4 \div \frac{1}{2}) + (1/2 \div 2) + (1\ \frac{1}{2} \div 8)$ $Fe = 0.500 + 0.25 + 0.188$ $Fe = 0.938$ |
| 63. | D | Subpart F, Table F-1 – Fire Extinguishers Data |
| 64. | D | 1926.350 (i) |
| 65. | A | 1926.51, Table D-1 |
| 66. | A | 1926.52 (d)(1), Table D-2 |
| 67. | A | Subpart F, Table F-1 – Fire Extinguishers Data |
| 68. | A | 1926.405 (a)(2)(ii)(G) |
| 69. | D | 1926.251 (c)(4)(iv) |
| 70. | B | 1926.200 (d) |
| 71. | C | 1926.250 (b)(1) |
| 72. | A | 1926.451 (b)(4) & (5) |
| 73. | B | See "Hole" in Glossary or 1926.500(b) |
| 74. | A | 1926.552 (c)(14)(ii) |
| 75. | A | 1926.300 (d)(3) |
| 76. | D | 1926.302 (b)(4) |
| 77. | D | 1926.302 (e)(7) |
| 78. | C | Subpart P, Appendix B, Table B-1 Maximum Allowable Slopes (Note 3) |
| 79. | C | 1926.1052 (c)(5) |
| 80. | D | 1926.703 (e)(2) |
| 81. | C | 1926.502 (g)(3)(iii) |
| 82. | B | 1926.652, Subpart P Appendix B, Figure B-1 Slope Configurations B-1.1 Excavations made in Type A soil |
| 83. | D | 1926.106 |
| 84. | C | 1926.651(b)(1) |
| 85. | C | 1926.451(a)(1) $1,000 \times 4 = 4,000$ $4,000 \div 2,000 = 2$ tons |

| Q | Answer | Section # |
|---|---|---|
| 86. | C | 1926.250(b)(7) |
| 87. | B | 1926.65 (n)(7) |
| 88. | C | 1926.62 (c)(1) |
| 89. | B | 1926.1101 (k)(9)(iv)(A) |
| 90. | B | 1926.651(g)(1)(i) |
| 91. | C | 1926.706(a)(2) |
| 92. | A | 1926.1101(c)(2) |
| 93. | C | 1926.104(c) |
| 94. | A | 1926.651(k)(1) |
| 95. | D | 1926.601(b)(6) |
| 96. | B | 1926.65 Appendix B, Part A, II |
| 97. | D | 1926.350(e)(2) |
| 98. | D | 1926.300(b)(4)(i) |
| 99. | B | 1926.652 Subpart P Appendix B, Figure B-1 Slope Configurations Figure B-1.3 Excavations Made in Type C Soil |
| 100. | B | 1926.250(b)(6) |
| 101. | A | 1926.54(c) |
| 102. | A | 1926.56, Table D-3 Minimum Illumination Intensities in Foot-Candles |
| 103. | C | 1926.51, Table D-1 |
| 104. | A | 1926.651(j)(2) |
| 105. | D | 1926.152(b)(3) |
| 106. | B | 1926.300(d)(2) |
| 107. | C | 1926.451(b)(4) |
| 108. | D | 1926.451(b)(7) |
| 109. | A | 1926.705(g) |
| 110. | D | 1926.502(g)(1)(ii) |
| 111. | C | 1926.703 (b)(8)(i) |
| 112. | A | 1926.706(b) |
| 113. | B | 1926.1053(a)(1)(i) |
| 114. | C | 1926.1053(b)(5)(i) 20 feet ÷ 4 feet = 5 feet |
| 115. | B | 1926.1101(j)(1)(i) |
| 116. | B | 1926.302(b)(3) |

| Q | Answer | Section # |
|---|--------|-----------|
| 117. | B | 1926.1053(a)(1)(ii) |
| 118. | A | 1926.51(a)(4) |
| 119. | B | 1926.102(a)(1) |
| 120. | B | 1926.56, Table D-3 Minimum Illumination Intensities in Foot-Candles |
| 121. | C | 1926.105(c)(1) |
| 122. | D | 1926.105(d) |
| 123. | B | 1926.250(b)(7) |
| 124. | B | 1926.250(b)(8)(iv) |
| 125. | A | 1926.451(a)(1) |
|  |  | 500 x 4 = 2,000 = 1 ton |
| 126. | B | 1926.604(a)(2)(i) |
| 127. | C | 1926.1052(a)(4) |
| 128. | B | 1926.652, Subpart P Appendix A (b) |
| 129. | C | 1926.652, Subpart P Appendix B, Table B-1 Maximum Allowable Slopes |
| 130. | D | 1926.652, Subpart P Appendix B, Figure B-1.1 Excavations made in Type A soil |
| 131. | C | 1926.652, Subpart P Appendix B, Figure B-1.4 Excavations Made in Layered Soils |
| 132. | C | 1926.704(c) |
| 133. | D | 1926.705(j) |
| 134. | D | 1926.652 Subpart P Appendix A (b)<br>Note: "Sand" is classified as Type C soil<br>1926.652 Subpart P Appendix B, Table B-1 Maximum Allowable Slopes |
| 135. | C | 1926.651(i)(1) |
| 136. | B | 1926.703(b)(8)(ii) |
| 137. | C | 1926.758(c) |
| 138. | D | 1926.651(a) |
| 139. | A | 1926.703(a)(2) |
| 140. | C | 1926.703(e)(1) |
| 141. | C | 1926.1408, Table A |
| 142. | C | 1926.252 (b) |
| 143. | B | 1926.300(b)(4)(iv)(a) |
| 144. | D | 1926.450(b), See "Self-contained Adjustable Scaffold" |
| 145. | C | 1926.451(g)(1) |
| 146. | B | 1926.756(a)(1) |

| Q | Answer | Section # |
|------|--------|-----------|
| 147. | B | 1926.451(c)(1)<br>Note: Not more than 4:1<br>4 x 4 feet = 16 feet |
| 148. | B | 1926.552(b)(3), 1926.552(c)(7) |
| 149. | D | 1926.454, Subpart L Appendix A, Scaffold Specifications, General Guidelines and Tables, 1.(b)(i) – Table<br>1926.454, Subpart L Appendix A, Scaffold Specifications, General Guidelines and Tables, 1.(c) – Table |
| 150. | C | 1926.454, Subpart L Appendix A, Scaffold Specifications, 2. General Guidelines and Tables (s)(1) |
| 151. | D | 1926.302(a)(1) |
| 152. | A | See "Kickout" in Glossary |
| 153. | A | 1926.454, Subpart L Appendix A, 1.(b)(ii) |
| 154. | C | 1926.502(d)(9) |
| 155. | D | 1926.454, Subpart L Appendix A, 1.(f) |
| 156. | C | 1926.404(b)(1)(ii) |
| 157. | A | 1926.604(2)(ii) |
| 158. | A | 1926.20(b)(3) |
| 159. | A | 1926.16(a) – (d) |
| 160. | A | 1926.50(d)(2), 1926.51(a)(4), 1926.51(c)(1), 1926.52, Table D-2 |
| 161. | D | 1926.651(g)(1)(i) |
| 162. | A | 1926.250(b)(1), 1926.250(b)(6), 1926.250(b)(7), 1926.250(b)(8)(iv) |
| 163. | D | 1926.301(b) – (d) |
| 164. | B | 1926.302(e)(2) |
| 165. | B | 1926.1101(b), See "Asbestos-containing material" (ACM) |
| 166. | B | 1926.300(b)(2) |
| 167. | D | 1926.652(e)(2) or 1926.652(g)(2) |
| 168. | B | 1926.21(b)(1) |
| 169. | D | 1926.51(c)(4) |
| 170. | C | 1926.652, Subpart P Appendix A, (b), See "Moist Soil" |
| 171. | D | 1926.251(b)(6)(i)(D) |
| 172. | C | 1926.702(b) |
| 173. | D | 1926.150, Table F-1 – Fire Extinguishers Data |
| 174. | D | 1926.761, Subpart R Appendix D, (2)(i) |

| Q | Answer | Section # |
|---|--------|-----------|
| 175. | A | 1926.302(e)(2) |
| 176. | C | 1926.152(d)(1) |
| 177. | B | 1926.454, Subpart L Appendix A, 2.(k) |
| 178. | C | 1926.502(b)(3) |
| 179. | C | 1926.451(h)(2)(ii) |
| 180. | B | 1926.302(b)(3) |
| 181. | A | 1926.302(a) |
| 182. | C | 1926.451(g) |
| 183. | B | 1926.452(w)(6)(i) |
| 184. | B | 1926.852(b) |
| 185. | B | 1926.452(h)(2) |
| 186. | D | 1926.502(f)(1)(i) |
| 187. | C | 1926.503, Subpart M Appendix A, (1) |

# Plumber Math Review

## The Problem of Math

Do you remember when you were in middle school or high school math class? There was always someone that would ask, "When am I ever going to use this?" Maybe that was you? The question is valid. Truthfully, many forms and levels of math are not directly applicable in daily life. So why did we have to study that math? Perhaps it is best to take a step back and recognize what math teaches beyond mechanical arithmetic. There is a level of analytic thinking achieved by the practice of math. Being able to see our problems in real life and all the variables involved and solve for desired outcomes *is* something we use every day.

Plumbing is one form of construction work that requires math knowledge. The most common math in plumbing is the calculation of measurements; this involves adding and subtracting fractions and converting decimals to fractions. Plumbing math also includes the understanding and use of basic geometry. A plumber might use the functions of a right triangle or the Pythagorean Theorem to calculate offsets. A plumber who has mastered this math is capable of precision in piping system layouts and can create impressive displays. Then there is money math. Anyone with a credit card and bank account should be capable of basic math to keep alive financially. Likewise, any plumber who wants to run a successful business will need to be good at math as it applies to money. Aside from not knowing why we study math, some people's bigger problem due to early math studies is a sense of deficiency or incompetence.

If you always excelled in math, you can skip the practice problems. But if you struggled in math at any point, you might have a deep underlying hatred for it. Math is one of the most common areas that potential plumbers view as obstacles. These negative emotions undermine their ability to succeed and sometimes stop them from attempting the examination altogether. But that is not going to be you! You are reading this book, and you are determined to succeed. Do not allow math to intimidate you anymore! You CAN do the math and pass the math portions of the examination! This positive thinking will open your mind to understanding math and empower you to succeed. Now that your mind is open to your own ability to succeed in math, it's time to review.

## General Knowledge Math

Imagine you are going exploring in the mountains. You might hike on a trail. But then you might also leave the trail to have a look around at other things. While leaving the trail will expose you to some interesting stuff. If you want to get where you are going, you need to stay on the course.

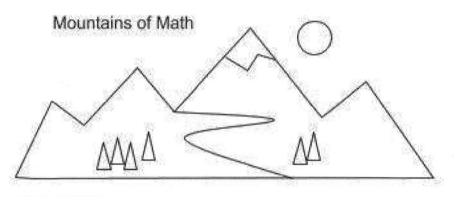

Figure 7-1

Math is like a vast mountain wilderness. There is so much to see! However, we cannot afford to get distracted. So, we will take the most direct path. This math review section is intended to focus only on the things you need to know to pass the examination.


## Math Operators

To solve the geometric functions of plumbers, you will need to be familiar with the basic math operators. These symbols tell us what to do with the numbers around them. In an equation, steps must be taken in a specific order. The following symbols have been listed in order of priority within the equation. (Do you remember the saying that goes along with this? "Please Excuse My Dear Aunt Sally" The first letter of each word is intended to help us remember the first letter of the operators - Parentheses, Exponent, Multiply, Divide, Add, Subtract.) This should be a basic review for you, but you will need to remember these operators and the order in which they are used for the examination.

| Operator | Name | Function |
|---|---|---|
| ( ) | Parentheses | Anything inside of the parentheses must be solved first |
| $a^2$ | Exponent | This indicates multiplying the number by itself. The "2" indicates there are two of the same number being multiplied together. |
| $\sqrt{}$ | Square Root | This operator breaks a number into the two numbers that, when multiplied together, produce the initial number. |
| $\times$ | Multiply | Multiply the numbers together. |
| $\div$ or / | Divide | Divide the number before the operator by the number after the operator; or divide the number on top by the number on bottom |
| + | Add | Add the numbers together. |
| - | Subtract | Subtract the number after the operator from the number before the operator. |

**Mathematics of Measurements**

Here is some math you *can* use in your daily life. In installing plumbing systems and fixtures, measurements are used all the time. True, a good calculator or app on your phone can do the calculations for you. Still, it is helpful to know how to do the math on paper or in your head.

**The Power of One**

As we proceed with math measurements, it is critical to consider what happens when we multiply anything by one. Do you remember what happens? Nothing, the number remains the same, right? But what if we change how "one" looks? What if it looks like this: 4/4? We still have one whole, but now we can see it has been divided into pieces, and as we use a fractioned whole as a multiplier, we can change how other numbers look as well. The amount has not changed, just the way it's presented.

Okay, tuck that into the back of your mind as we go on here...

## Fraction Review

A fraction is a part or portion of a whole. It is helpful to visualize fractions as pieces of a pie. For example, you cut a pie into eight pieces to share it with 4 of your friends. You and each friend receive one part of the pie (⅛). After everyone has eaten ⅝ of the pie is gone. You put ⅜ back in the fridge for tomorrow.

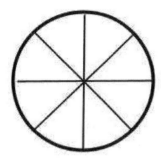

Fractions of a Pie

Portions like this are also easy to see on a measuring tape to measure to the fraction of an inch.

As we review how a fraction is written, it is essential to remember that the numerator is the number on top, which indicates how much of the whole is counted. The denominator is on the bottom, how many pieces the whole number was divided into.

| Task | Method | Example |
|------|--------|---------|
| Multiplying Fractional Measurements | Step 1:  Multiply the numerator by the numerator<br><br>Step 2: the denominator by the denominator<br><br>Step 3: Simplify the fraction if possible | Multiply ½ by ¾ .<br><br>Step 1: 1 x 3 = 3<br><br>Step 2: 2 x 4 = 8<br><br>Step 3: ⅜ does not need to be simplified. |
| Simplify Fractions | Step 1:  Examine the numerator and denominator to see if there is a number that both can be divided by evenly (most often 2 or 4)<br><br>Step 2: Divide the numerator by that number.<br><br>Step 3:Divide the denominator by that number.<br><br>Step 4: Write as a fraction | Simplify 10/16".<br><br>Step 1: Can be divided by 2 evenly.<br><br>Step 2: 10 ÷ 2 = 5<br><br>Step 3: 16 ÷ 2 = 8<br><br>Step 4: ⅝" |
| Adding Fractional Measurements | Step 1: Convert fractions to get common denominator, when necessary<br><br>Step 2: Add the numerators, and keep the same denominator<br><br>Step 3: Simply the fraction | Add 7/16" to ¾".<br><br>Step 1: (¾" x 4/4) = 12/16"<br><br>Step 2: 7/16" + 12/16" = 19/16"<br><br>Step 3: 19/16" = 16/16" + 3/16" = **1 3/16"** |
| Subtracting Fractional Measurements | Step 1: Convert fractions to get common denominator, when necessary<br><br>Step 2: Subtract the numerators, and keep the same denominator.<br><br>Step 3: Simply the fraction | Subtract ⅝" from 1 ¼" .<br><br>Step 1:  1 ¼" = 4/4 + ¼ = 5/4" x 2/2 = 10/8"<br><br>Step 2:  10/8" - ⅝" = ⅝"<br><br>Step 3:  ⅝" does not need to be simplified. |

125

## Conversion of Length Measurements

| Conversion | Method | Example |
|---|---|---|
| Fractional Inches to Decimal Inches | Step 1: Divide the fractional inch numerator by the denominator <br> Step 2: Add the decimal form to the whole number. | Convert 5 ⅜" to decimal inches. <br><br> Step 1: $3 \div 8 = 0.375$" <br><br> Step 2: $5" + 0.375" = $ **5.375"** |
| Decimal Inches to Fractional Inches | Step 1: Multiply the decimal by 16 <br> Step 2: Round the new decimal to the nearest whole number, <br> Step 3: Put that number as the numerator over 16. <br> Step 4: Simplify the fraction if possible. <br> Step 5: Add the fractional inches to the whole number of inches | Convert 8.65" to fractional inches. <br><br> Step 1: $0.65" \times 16 = 10.4$ <br><br> **Step 2: $10.4 \approx 10$** <br><br> Step 3: 10/16 <br><br> Step 4: $10/16 \div 2/2 = $ ⅝" <br><br> Step 5: $8" + $ ⅝" $= $ **8 ⅝"** |
| Feet and Fractional Inches to Decimal Feet | Step 1: Convert fractional inches to decimal inches (see above). <br> Step 2: Divide by 12 <br> Step 3: Add the decimal to the whole number of feet. | Convert 10' 9 ¾" to decimal feet. <br><br> Step 1: $9 ¾" = 9 + (3 \div 4) = 9 + 0.75 = 9.75$" <br><br> Step 2: $9.75" \div 12 = 0.813$' <br><br> Step 3: $10' + 0.813' = $ **10.813'** |
| Decimal Feet to Feet and Fractional Inches | Step 1: Convert Decimal feet to inches by multiplying by 12 <br> Step 2: Convert decimal inches to fractional inches (see above) <br> Step 3: Put the fractional inch measurement together with the whole number of feet. | Convert 14.143' to feet and fractional inches. <br><br> Step 1: $0.143 \times 12 = 1.716$" <br><br> Step 2: $1.716" = 1" + (.716 \times 16/16) = 1" + 11/16" = 1 \ 11/16$" <br><br> Step 3: **14' 1 11/16"** |

Note: Decimal feet are also known as "engineer measurements". Feet, inches, and fractions of an inch are also known as "field measurements."

## Conversion of Length Measurements - Practice Problems

| Number | Question | Answer |
|--------|----------|--------|
| 1. | Convert 2 3/8" to decimal inches.<br><br>A. 2.25"<br>B. 2.375"<br>C. 2.43"<br>D. 2.5" | |
| 2. | Convert 5 5/16" to decimal inches.<br><br>A. 5.125"<br>B. 5.25"<br>C. 5.312"<br>D. 5.375" | |
| 3. | Convert 7 15/16" to decimal inches.<br><br>A. 7.875"<br>B. 7.915"<br>C. 7.937"<br>D. 7.947" | |
| 4. | Convert 4 13/16" to decimal inches.<br><br>A. 4.789"<br>B. 4.812"<br>C. 4.834"<br>D. 4.878" | |
| 5. | Convert 6.187" to fractional inches.<br><br>A. 6 1/8"<br>B. 6 3/16"<br>C. 6 5/16"<br>D. 6 7/16" | |
| 6. | Convert 9.625" to fractional inches.<br><br>A. 9 1/2"<br>B. 9 9/16"<br>C. 9 5/8"<br>D. 9 11/16" | |
| 7. | Convert 4.125" to fractional inches.<br><br>A. 4 1/8"<br>B. 4 3/16"<br>C. 4 5/16"<br>D. 4 7/16" | |

| | | |
|---|---|---|
| 8. | Convert 8.875" to fractional inches.<br><br>A. 8 3/4"<br>B. 8 13/16"<br>C. 8 7/8"<br>D. 8 15/16" | |
| 9. | Convert 12' 9 1/4" to decimal feet.<br><br>A. 12.65'<br>B. 12.77'<br>C. 12.85'<br>D. 12.90' | |
| 10. | Convert 15' 11 3/4" to decimal feet.<br><br>A. 15.65'<br>B. 15.87'<br>C. 15.93'<br>D. 15.98' | |
| 11. | Convert 4' 6 1/2" to decimal feet.<br><br>A. 4.45'<br>B. 4.51'<br>C. 4.54'<br>D. 4.60' | |
| 12. | Convert 2' 2 1/2" to decimal feet.<br><br>A. 2.21'<br>B. 2.25'<br>C. 2.29'<br>D. 2.33' | |
| 13. | Convert 16.71' to feet and fractional inches.<br><br>A. 16' 7 1/2"<br>B. 16' 8"<br>C. 16' 8 1/2"<br>D. 16' 9" | |
| 14. | Convert 6.75' to feet and fractional inches.<br><br>A. 6' 7"<br>B. 6' 8"<br>C. 6' 8 1/2"<br>D. 6' 9" | |

| 15. | Convert 21.125' to feet and fractional inches.<br><br>A. 21' 0 1/2"<br>B. 21' 1"<br>C. 21' 1 1/2"<br>D. 21' 2" | |
|---|---|---|
| 16. | Convert 18.83' to feet and fractional inches.<br><br>A. 18' 7 1/2"<br>B. 18' 8"<br>C. 18' 9"<br>D. 18' 10" | |

## Area

A plumber may occasionally need to figure out a surface area. Area measurements are a matter of multiplication. Consider the examples below:

| Area Shape | Formula | Example |
|---|---|---|
| Square | Area = Side x Side | Find the area of a square that is 6" on each side.<br><br>Area = 6" x 6"<br>Area = **36 in.$^2$** |
| Rectangle | Area = Length x Width | Find the area of a room that is 13' 6" in width and 15' in length.<br><br>Area = 13.5' x 15'<br>Area = **202.5 ft$^2$** |
| Circle | Area = $\pi$ x radius$^2$<br><br>(hints: Remember the radius is ½ of the diameter. $\pi$ = 3.14) | Find the area of a tank that has a diameter of 16 feet.<br><br>Area = 3.14 x (8)$^2$<br>Area = 3.14 x 64<br>Area = **200.96 ft$^2$** |

## Area - Practice Problems

| Number | Question | Answer |
|--------|----------|--------|
| 1. | Find the area of a square that is 8" on each side.<br><br>A. 56 square inches<br>B. 64 square inches<br>C. 72 square inches<br>D. 80 square inches | |
| 2. | Find the area of a square that is 24' 3" on each side.<br><br>A. 466 square feet<br>B. 498 square feet<br>C. 554 square feet<br>D. 588 square feet | |
| 3. | Find the area of a room that is 8' 6" in width and 16' in length.<br><br>A. 112 square feet<br>B. 124 square feet<br>C. 136 square feet<br>D. 156 square feet | |
| 4. | Find the area of a room that is 24' in width and 30' in length.<br><br>A. 720 square feet<br>B. 740 square feet<br>C. 782 square feet<br>D. 824 square feet | |
| 5. | Find the area of a tank that has a diameter of 12 feet.<br><br>A. 97 square feet<br>B. 113 square feet<br>C. 124 square feet<br>D. 132 square feet | |
| 6. | Find the area of a tank that has a diameter of 20 inches.<br><br>A. 256 square inches<br>B. 284 square inches<br>C. 314 square inches<br>D. 338 square inches | |

## Volume

Okay, now that you have reviewed area formulas, let's do some volume. Again, most of this is basic multiplication.

| Volume Shape | Formula | Example |
|---|---|---|
| Rectangular Prism | Volume = Length x Width x Height | Find the volume of a tub that is 20" wide, 56" long and 14" deep on inside dimensions.<br><br>Volume = 20" x 56" x 14"<br>Volume = **15,680 in³** |
| Cylinder | Area = **π** x radius² x Height | Calculate the volume of a cylindrical tank that has a diameter of 18" and a height of 50".<br><br>Volume = 3.14 x (9)² x 50<br>Volume = 3.14 x 81 x 50<br>Volume = **12,717 in³** |

The examples above demonstrate using the formulas, but the result is a volume in *cubic inches*. Most of the time, volume is *not* expressed in cubic inches. It is in cubic feet or gallons. It is essential to know how to convert cubic inches into cubic feet and vice versa.

## Volume - Practice Problems

| Number | Question | Answer |
|--------|----------|--------|
| 1. | Find the volume of a tub that is 16" wide, 60" long and 16" deep on inside dimensions.<br><br>A. 960 cubic inches<br>B. 15,360 cubic inches<br>C. 256 cubic inches<br>D. 1536 cubic inches | |
| 2. | Find the volume of a rectangular aquarium that is 12" wide, 48" long and 16" deep on inside dimensions.<br><br>A. 9216 cubic inches<br>B. 8064 cubic inches<br>C. 8640 cubic inches<br>D. 8832 cubic inches | |
| 3. | Calculate the volume of a cylindrical tank that has a diameter of 20" and a height of 48".<br>(Use Pi = 3.14)<br><br>A. 14904 cubic inches<br>B. 15072 cubic inches<br>C. 15112 cubic inches<br>D. 15222 cubic inches | |
| 4. | Calculate the volume of a cylindrical tank that has a diameter of 10' and a height of 6'. (Use Pi = 3.14)<br><br>A. 188 cubic feet<br>B. 471 cubic feet<br>C. 1884 cubic feet<br>D. 94 cubic feet | |

## Converting Cubic Inches to Cubic Feet

CAUTION: COMMON ERROR! Often, when we need to convert cubic inches into cubic feet, we simply want to multiply by 12. That is fine for linear measurement, but we are not talking about measurements on tape. This is volume, and there is a big difference! So, we must remember it this way:

**One Cubic Foot = 1 foot x 1 foot x 1 foot = 1 ft$^3$**

Okay, now replace each of the 1-foot measurements with 12 inches because they are the same length.

**One Cubic Foot = 12 inches x 12 inches x 12 inches**

Now you can do the multiplication.

**One Cubic Foot = 12 x 12 x 12 = 1728 in$^3$**

Ah-hah! Now you have your conversion number. Let's take the numbers we calculated above and convert them to cubic feet!

| Measurement | Conversion to Cubic Feet | Example |
|---|---|---|
| **15,680 in$^3$** | Divide by 1728 in$^3$ to get cubic feet. | 15,680 in$^3$ ÷ 1728 in$^3$ = **9.07 ft$^3$** |
| **12,717 in$^3$** | | 12,717 in$^3$ ÷ 1728 in$^3$ = **7.36 ft$^3$** |

## Cubic Inches to Cubic Feet Practice Problems

| Number | Question | Answer |
|--------|----------|--------|
| 1. | Convert 10,368 cubic inches into cubic feet.<br><br>A. 4 cubic feet<br>B. 5 cubic feet<br>C. 6 cubic feet<br>D. 8 cubic feet | |
| 2. | Convert 43,200 cubic inches into cubic feet.<br><br>A. 21 cubic feet<br>B. 25 cubic feet<br>C. 27 cubic feet<br>D. 28 cubic feet | |
| 3. | Convert 25,920 cubic inches into cubic feet.<br><br>A. 12 cubic feet<br>B. 14 cubic feet<br>C. 15 cubic feet<br>D. 16 cubic feet | |
| 4. | Convert 63,936 cubic inches into cubic feet.<br><br>A. 37 cubic feet<br>B. 39 cubic feet<br>C. 41 cubic feet<br>D. 43 cubic feet | |

## Converting Cubic Feet into Gallons

If you had a container that was exactly one foot in length, width, and height, you could put one cubic foot of water into the container, right? Yes. So, if you have that container, and you are filling it up with a one-gallon milk jug, how many times would you have to refill the milk jug to fill the container?

Well, let's save time on actually doing that experiment and take it from those who already have! It would take seven and a half gallons to fill the container, or more precisely **7.48 gallons.** This is our conversion number! To find the number of gallons in a cubic foot volume, multiply by **7.48**!

On the other hand, if you have a gallon measurement, and you need to find out how many cubic feet you have, simply divide the cubic feet by **7.48**!

Let's continue using the numbers from above and convert them to gallons.

| Measurement | Cubic Feet to Gallons | Example |
|---|---|---|
| **9.07 ft³** | Multiply cubic feet by 7.48 for gallons. | 9.07 ft³ x 7.48 = **67.84 gallons** |
| **7.36 ft³** | | 7.36 ft³ x 7.48 = **55.05 gallons** |

| Measurement | Gallons To Cubic Feet | Example |
|---|---|---|
| **112 gallons** | Divide gallons by 7.48 for cubic feet.. | 112 gallons ÷ 7.48 = **15 ft³** |
| **561 gallons** | | 561 gallons ÷ 7.48 = **75 ft³** |

## Cubic Feet to Gallons - Practice Problems

| Number | Question | Answer |
|--------|----------|--------|
| 1. | Convert 6.68 cubic feet into gallons. A. 30 gallons B. 40 gallons C. 50 gallons D. 60 gallons | |
| 2. | Convert 13.36 cubic feet into gallons. A. 70 gallons B. 80 gallons C. 90 gallons D. 100 gallons | |
| 3. | Convert 90 gallons to cubic feet. A. 10 cubic feet B. 12 cubic feet C. 14 cubic feet D. 16 cubic feet | |
| 4. | Convert 449 gallons to cubic feet. A. 60 cubic feet B. 65 cubic feet C. 70 cubic feet D. 75 cubic feet | |

## Converting Gallons into Pounds

Weight is expressed most commonly in pounds. If you were to put a gallon jug of water on a scale and subtract the weight of the container, you would find that water weighs **8.33** pounds (LBS). So to find the weight of a volume in gallons, simply multiply by **8.33.**

Being able to calculate the weight of water in the pipes is a useful skill for a plumber. Let's take our measurements from above and, once again, convert them, this time into pounds.

| Measurement | Conversion to Gallons | Example |
|---|---|---|
| **67.84 gallons** | Multiply gallons by 8.33 for pounds. | 67.84 x 8.33 = **565.1 lbs** |
| **55.05 gallons** | | 55.05 x 8.33 = **458.56 lbs** |

## Gallons to Pounds - Practice Problems

| Number | Question | Answer |
|---|---|---|
| 1. | Convert 50 gallons into weight measurement in pounds.<br><br>A. 380 pounds<br>B. 406 pounds<br>C. 416 pounds<br>D. 444 pounds | |
| 2. | Convert 10 gallons into weight measurement in pounds.<br><br>A. 62 pounds<br>B. 74 pounds<br>C. 83 pounds<br>D. 91 pounds | |
| 3. | Convert 5 gallons into weight measurement in pounds.<br><br>A. 32 pounds<br>B. 36 pounds<br>C. 39 pounds<br>D. 42 pounds | |

## Offsets

Calculating for an offset is one of the math skills you will need to pass your examination. According to the International Plumbing Code, an offset is "a combination of approved bends that makes two changes in direction bringing one section of the pipe out of line but into a line parallel with the other section."

Or in other words, the pipe is running along, but it has to shift the centerline over while still going in the same direction. This is usually to go around an obstacle. Offsets can be created using 90-degree, 45-degree, or other angled fittings, so long as both of the fittings are the same degree angle. There is not much math needed if 90-degree fittings are used. Most commonly, offset calculations are based on 45-degree fittings. Let's review how that is done.

To do calculations relating to a 45-degree offset, we need to be able to visualize the triangle created by the offset. The angled pipe is the *diagonal* of the triangle. The *offset* is the distance the center of the pipe has moved over from its original location. The *run* is how far the pipe travels as it is angling over to the new central location. (See figure 7-2.)

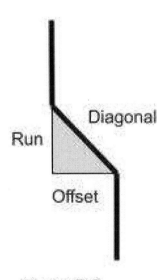

Figure 7-2

To complete our calculations, we need to understand the right triangle with two 45 degree angles. This triangle has two sides that are the same length, A and B. (See figure 7-3). If we know the length of A, then we also know the length of B because they are the same. Most often, we are calculating for the diagonal C because that is where the pipe will run. To calculate C, multiply the offset B by 1.414.

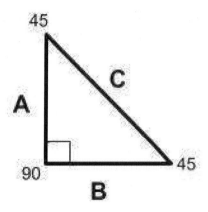

Figure 7-3

Example: Calculate the diagonal for a pipe with an offset of 5 inches and convert the decimal to fractions of an inch. (See figure 7-4)

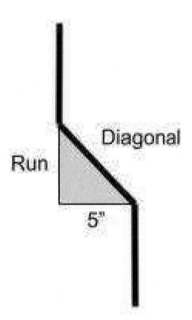

Figure 7-4

|  | Formula or Method | Example |
|---|---|---|
| 5" | Offset x 1.414 = Diagonal | 5" x 1.414 = 7.07" |
| Decimal Inches to Fractional Inches | Step 1: Multiply the decimal by 16<br>Step 2: Round the new decimal to the nearest whole number,<br>Step 3: Put that number as the numerator over 16.<br>Step 4: Simplify the fraction if possible.<br>Step 5: Add the fractional inches to the whole number of inches | Convert 7.07" to fractional inches.<br><br>Step 1: .07" x 16 = 1.12<br><br>Step 2: 1.12 ≈ 1<br><br>Step 3: 1/16<br><br>Step 4: not necessary<br><br>Step 5: 7" + 1/16" = **7 1/16"** |

**Offsets - Practice Problems**

| Number | Question | Answer |
|---|---|---|
| 1. | Calculate the diagonal for a pipe that offsets 21 inches using two 45 degree fittings.<br><br>A. 25.5 inches.<br>B. 27.8 inches<br>C. 29.7 inches<br>D. 31.2 inches | |
| 2. | Calculate the diagonal for a pipe that offsets 12 inches using two 45 degree fittings.<br><br>A. 13.2 inches.<br>B. 14.8 inches<br>C. 15.7 inches<br>D. 16.9 inches | |
| 3. | Calculate the diagonal for a pipe that offsets 6 inches using two 45 degree fittings.<br><br>A. 5.8 inches.<br>B. 6.4 inches<br>C. 7 inches<br>D. 8.5 inches | |
| 4. | Calculate the diagonal for a pipe that offsets 14 inches using two 45 degree fittings.<br><br>A. 18.4 inches.<br>B. 19.8 inches<br>C. 21.3 inches<br>D. 24.5 inches | |

## Pythagorean Theorem and 1.414

Hopefully, your plumbing education has already shown you how essential it is to remember the number 1.414. If not, let us emphasize that now. You should have the number 1.414 locked inside your memory forever if you are a plumber. Have you ever wondered where it came from?

We must go several thousands of years back to a Greek philosopher named Pythagoras to answer that question. One day, he examined triangles and found the relationship between the three sides of a right triangle. This made it possible to figure out any side of the triangle if the other two sides were known. He discovered that if you square the number of the two shorter sides and add them together, the total area will be the same as the square of the longer diagonal side every time! Genius! (See figures 7-5 and 7-6).

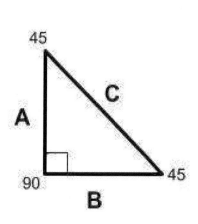

Figure 7-5

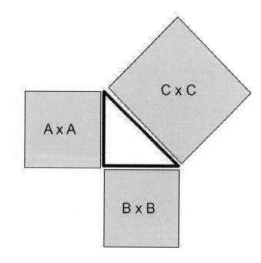

Figure 7-6

Formula: $A^2 + B^2 = C^2$

To understand the origins of the number **1.414**, we need only solve the Pythagorean Theorem using a 45-degree triangle that has two sides that are 1 unit of measure in length. (See figure 7-7)

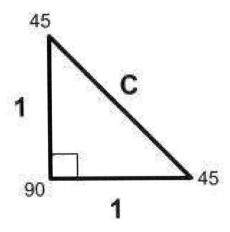

Figure 7-7

To solve for C, put the number 1 into the formula for both A and B.

Formula: $A^2 + B^2 = C^2$

| Solving for C | Method | Example |
|---|---|---|
| Step 1: | Rewrite the Pythagorean Theorem with the two known sides. | $(1)^2 + (1)^2 = C^2$ |
| Step 2: | Square the numbers | $1 + 1 = C^2$ |
| Step 3: | Add the squared numbers together | $2 = C^2$ |
| Step 4: | Take the square root of the added numbers (use a calculator) | $\sqrt{2} = \sqrt{C^2}$ |
| Step 5: | Write the answer for C | **1.414 = C** |

Do you see what we just accomplished?  We came up with the constant 1.414, which we can use on any triangle with two 45 degree angles to calculate the diagonal!

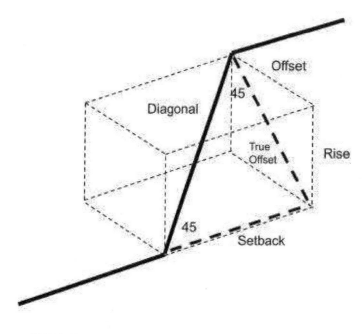

Figure 7-8

## Rolling Offsets

A rolling offset refers to a situation where the center of the pipe has moved both horizontally and vertically. The two pipes are running in the same direction and connected by a diagonal. (See figure 7-8)

This rolling offset is created by two 45-degree elbows. Therefore, the triangle creating the diagonal is a triangle with two 45-degree angles and two sides that are the same. However, it is leaning to the side. To find the diagonal for this triangle, we must first find the diagonal of another triangle. (See figure 7-9) This triangle consists of two sides, the *offset* and the *rise*, and the diagonal, which we will call the *true offset*. Often the *offset* and the *rise* are different lengths, but they can also be the same.

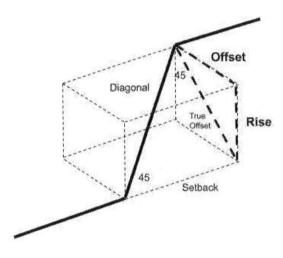

Figure 7-9

It is important to note that the *true offset* and the *setback* are both the same length, which is consistent with any triangle with two 45-degree angles. If we know the *rise* and the *offset*, then we can solve for the *true offset* using the Pythagorean Theorem. Once we know what the *true offset* is, we can multiply that number by 1.414 to find the *diagonal*. This is an important step, not to be overlooked. Sometimes plumbers get so excited when they have completed the calculations for the *true offset* using the Pythagorean Theorem that they forget to take the last step and multiply by 1.414 to get the *diagonal*. Do not forget this critical step!

**Example**: Find the diagonal for a rolling offset if the rise is 3 feet and the offset is 5 feet.

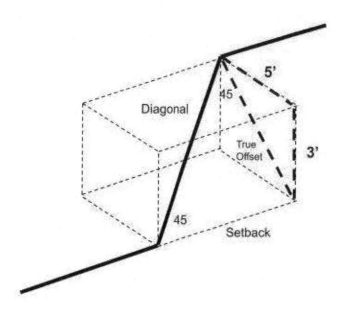

Figure 7-10

| Solve for Diagonal | Method | Example |
|---|---|---|
| Step 1: | Rewrite the Pythagorean Theorem with the two known sides. | $(3)^2 + (5)^2 = C^2$ |
| Step 2: | Square the numbers | $9 + 25 = C^2$ |
| Step 3: | Add the squared numbers together | $34 = C^2$ |
| Step 4: | Take the square root of the added numbers (use a calculator) | $\sqrt{34} = \sqrt{C^2}$ |
| Step 5: | Write the answer for C (*true offset*) | $5.83 = C$ |
| Step 6: | Multiply C by 1.414 to get *diagonal* | $5.83 \times 1.414 = \textbf{8.24'}$ |

Convert Decimal Feet to Field Measurements

| Decimal Feet to Feet and Fractional Inches | Step 1: Convert Decimal feet to inches by multiplying by 12<br>Step 2: Convert decimal inches to fractional inches (see above)<br>Step 3: Put the fractional inch measurement together with the whole number of feet. | Step 1: 0.24 x 12 = 2.88"<br><br>Step 2: 2.88" = 2" + (0.88 x 16/16) = 2" + 14/16" = 2 14/16" = 2 ⅞"<br><br>Step 3: **8' 2 7/8"** |
|---|---|---|

## **Rolling Offset - Practice Problems**

| Number | Question | Answer |
|---|---|---|
| 1. | Calculate the diagonal for a rolling offset made with two 45 degree fittings which has a rise of 6 inches and an offset of 8 inches.<br><br>A. 12.5 inches<br>B. 14.1 inches<br>C. 15.3 inches<br>D. 16.7 inches | |
| 2. | Calculate the diagonal for a rolling offset made with two 45 degree fittings which has a rise of 20 inches and an offset of 15 inches.<br><br>A. 32.65 inches<br>B. 33.86 inches<br>C. 34.73 inches<br>D. 35.35 inches | |
| 3. | Calculate the diagonal for a rolling offset made with two 45 degree fittings which has a rise of 16 inches and an offset of 3 inches.<br><br>A. 23.01 inches<br>B. 23.35 inches<br>C. 23.64 inches<br>D. 23. 87 inches | |
| 4. | Calculate the diagonal for a rolling offset made with two 45 degree fittings which has a rise of 15 inches and an offset of 5 inches.<br><br>A. 23.36 inches<br>B. 23.45 inches<br>C. 23.56 inches<br>D. 23.75 inches | |

### 45° Offsets in Parallel

At times multiple pipes are run parallel to each other. If these pipes were both to offset in the same proportions, some adjustments would need to be made to the lengths around the offset to keep uniform spacing. (See Figure 5-11)

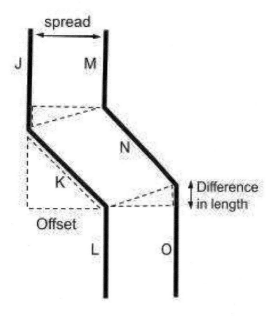

Figure 7-11

In Figure 7-11, you can see the two pipes maintain an equal *spread*. The *diagonals* K and N are the same length. However, the pipes above and below the *diagonals* are different. The calculated difference allows the pipes to maintain equal spacing. As we consider the difference in lengths, we can observe a new triangle. This triangle has three sides of different lengths: *spread, difference, diagonal*. (See Figure 7-12) The *diagonal* will not be needed to find the difference in length. To calculate the difference, simply multiply the spread by **0.414**.

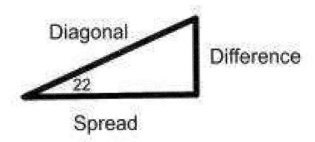

Figure 7-12

At this point, we could dig pretty deep into the geometry behind the number 0.414, but that would be taking us off course. So, for now, if you will remember the number 0.414, you will be able to do these calculations. You already know the number 1.414. If you remember to drop the whole one off the front, you will have what you need.

**Example:** Calculate the length for M, N, and O if J equals 12", L equals 14", and the offset equals 10". The spread is 8".

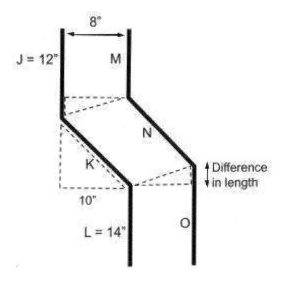

Figure 7-13

| Solve for M | Method | Example |
|---|---|---|
| Step 1: | Multiply the spread by 0.414 | 8" x 0.414 = 3.312" |
| Step 2: | Subtract the difference in length from J. | 12" - 3.312" = 8.688" or 8 11/16" |
| | | **M = 8 11/16"** |
| | | |
| Solve for N | | |
| Step 1: | Multiply the offset by 1.414 to get K. | 10" x 1.414 = 14.14" or 14 ⅛" |
| Step 2: | Remember N is the same as K. | **N = 14 ⅛"** |
| | | |
| Solve for O | | |
| Step 1: | Multiply the spread by 0.414 | 8" x 0.414 = 3.312" |
| Step 2: | Add the difference in length to L. | 14" + 3.312" = 17.312" or 17 5/16" |
| | | **O =17 5/16"** |

### 45 Degree Offsets in Parallel - Practice Problems

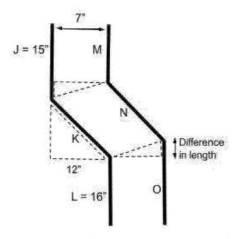

Practice Problem Figure 1

| Number | Question | Answer |
|--------|----------|--------|
| 1. | Calculate the measurement for M if the spread between pipes in parallel is 7" and J is 15". See Practice Problem Figure 1<br><br>A. 11 5/8"<br>B. 11 7/8"<br>C. 12 1/8"<br>D. 12 3/8" | |
| 2. | Calculate the measurement for N if the offset between pipes in parallel is 12". See Practice Problem Figure 1<br><br>A. 16 15/16"<br>B. 17 1/8"<br>C. 17 1/4"<br>D. 17 3/8" | |
| 3. | Calculate the measurement for O if the spread between pipes is 7" and L is 16". See Practice Problem Figure 1<br><br>A. 18 3/8"<br>B. 18 1/2"<br>C. 18 5/8"<br>D. 18 7/8" | |

## Special Case 45° Offsets in Parallel

Special case 45° offsets in parallel refer to the use of 45-degree fittings to create a 90° bend. (See Figure 7-14) Notice that we are dealing with two pipes that have an equal spread and that this setup creates the same smaller triangles we dealt with when calculating 45° offsets in parallel. The difference in length can again be calculated by multiplying the *spread* by **0.414.** However, on the inside pipe with sections M and O, the difference will be subtracted from sections J and L, respectively. In the case of section N, the difference will be subtracted *twice* from the length of section K.

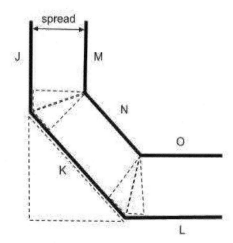

Figure 7-14

**Example**: Calculate the lengths for M, N and O from the measurements given in Figure 7-15.

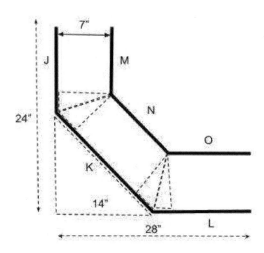

Figure 7-15

152

| Solve for M | Method | Example |
|---|---|---|
| Step 1: | Find J by subtracting the side of the triangle at the bottom from the overall length. | 24" - 14" = 10"<br>**J = 10"** |
| Step 2: | Multiply the spread by 0.414 to get the difference in length. | 7" x 0.414 = 2.89" |
| Step 3: | Subtract the difference in length from J. | 10" - 2.89" = 7.11" or 7 1/8" |
| | | **M = 7 1/8"** |
| | | |
| Solve for N | | |
| Step 1: | Multiply the side of the triangle at the bottom by 1.414 to get K. | 14" x 1.414 = 19.79" or 14 ⅛"<br>**K = 14 ⅛"** |
| Step 2: | Multiply the spread by 0.414 to get the difference in length. | 7" x 0.414 = 2.98" |
| Step 3: | Subtract the difference in length from K two times to get N. | 19.79" - (2 x 2.98") = N<br>19.79" - 5.96" = N<br>13.83 = N<br>**N = 13 13/16"** |
| | | |
| Solve for O | | |
| Step 1: | Find L by subtracting the side of the triangle at the bottom from the overall length. | 28" - 14" = 14"<br>**L = 14"** |
| Step 2: | Multiply the spread by 0.414 to get the difference in length. | 7" x 0.414 = 2.98" |
| Step 3: | Subtract the difference in length from L. | 14" - 2.98" =11.02" or 11"<br>**O = 11"** |

## Special Case 45° Offsets in Parallel - Practice Problem

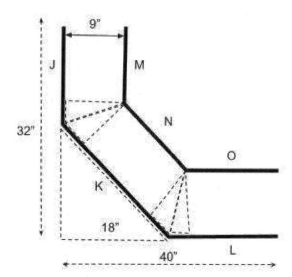

Practice Problem Figure 2

| Number | Question | Answer |
|--------|----------|--------|
| 1. | Calculate the measurement for a special case 90 degree offset using 45 degree elbows for M if the spread between pipes is 9". See Practice Problem Figure 2<br><br>A. 10 1/8"<br>B. 10 1/4"<br>C. 10 3/8"<br>D. 10 1/2" | |
| 2. | Calculate the measurement for a special case 90 degree offset using 45 degree elbows for N if the spread between pipes is 9". See Practice Problem Figure 2<br><br>A. 17 5/8"<br>B. 17 7/8"<br>C. 18"<br>D. 18 3/8" | |
| 3. | Calculate the measurement for a special case 90 degree offset using 45 degree elbows for O if the spread between pipes is 9". See Practice Problem Figure 2<br><br>A. 18 1/8"<br>B. 18 1/4"<br>C. 18 3/8"<br>D. 18 5/8" | |

## Calculating the Slope of Drainage Pipes

You are well aware of the importance of slope in drainage pipes by now. It is the slope that carries the waste away. You might use this already in your daily work, but let's review. The words slope, grade, and pitch are often used interchangeably. We will refer to the slope as *grade*. The *run* is the horizontal distance traveled by the pipe. The *drop* is the vertical distance the pipe has dropped because of the grade. (See Figure 7-16)

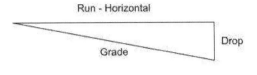

Figure 7-16

*Grade* is most often expressed in inches per foot or a percentage. There are several useful formulas for calculating the *grade*. To calculate correctly, you may need to convert feet to inches or inches to feet.

## Grade

$$\text{Grade} = \frac{\text{Drop} \quad \leftarrow \text{Inches}}{\text{Run} \quad \leftarrow \text{Feet}}$$

Figure 7-17

155

**Example**: Find the grade if the *drop* is 8 inches and the *run* is 64 feet. (Figure 7-18)

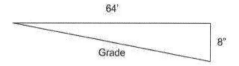

Figure 7-18

| Find Grade | Method | Example |
|---|---|---|
| Step 1: | Divide the drop by the run. | 8 ÷ 64 = 0.125 |
| Step 2: | Convert decimal to fraction. | 0.125 x 16/16 = 2/16 = 1/8 |
| Step 3: | Write grade in inches per foot. | Grade = ⅛" per foot |

**Drop**

Drop = Grade x Run

Figure 7-19

**Example**: Find the drop if the grade is ¼" per foot and the run is 25 feet. (Figure 7-20)

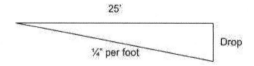

Figure 7-20

| Find Drop | Method | Example |
|---|---|---|
| Step 1: | Multiply the grade by the run. | ¼" x 25' = 25/4" |
| Step 2: | Reduce fraction. | 25/4 = 6 ¼" = drop |

## Percent Grade

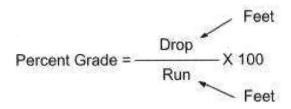

Figure 7-21

**Example**: Find the percentage grade if the drop is 30 inches and the run is 120 feet. (Figure 7-22)

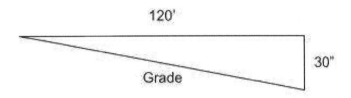

Figure 7-22

| Find Percent Grade | Method | Example |
|---|---|---|
| Step 1: | Convert the drop from inches into feet. | 30" ÷ 12 = 2.5 feet |
| Step 2: | Divide the drop by the run. | 2.5 ÷ 120 = 0.02 |
| Step 3: | Multiply by 100. | 0.02 x 100 = 2 |
| Step 4: | Write as a percent. | 2% grade |

## Drop from Percent Grade

$$Drop = \frac{Percent\ Grade \times Run}{100}$$

Note: Drop will be in the same units of measure as the Run.

Figure 7-23

**Example**: Find the drop if the percentage grade is 1% and the run is 75 feet.  (Figure 7-24)

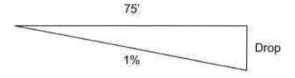

Figure 7-24

| Find Percentage Grade | Method | Example |
|---|---|---|
| Step 1: | Multiply the percentage grade by the run. | 1 x 75 = 75 |
| Step 2: | Divide by 100. | 75 ÷ 100 = .75 feet |
| Step 3: | Convert to inches. | .75 feet x 12 inches = 9 inches |

## Grade, Drop and Percentage Grade - Practice Problems

| Number | Question | Answer |
|--------|----------|--------|
| 1. | Find the grade of a pipe if the drop is 18 3/4" and the run is 75 feet.<br><br>A. 1/16" per foot<br>B. 1/8" per foot<br>C. 1/4" per foot<br>D. 1/2" per foot | |
| 2. | Find the grade of a pipe if the drop is 12 1/2" and the run is 25 feet.<br><br>A. 1/16" per foot<br>B. 1/8" per foot<br>C. 1/4" per foot<br>D. 1/2" per foot | |
| 3. | Find the grade of a pipe if the drop is 12 1/2" and the run is 200 feet.<br>A. 1/16" per foot<br>B. 1/8" per foot<br>C. 1/4" per foot<br>D. 1/2" per foot | |
| 4. | Find the drop if the grade is 1/4" per foot and the run is 50 feet.<br><br>A. 12 1/4"<br>B. 12 1/2"<br>C. 12 3/4"<br>D. 13" | |
| 5. | Find the drop if the grade is 1/4" per foot and the run is 80 feet.<br><br>A. 20"<br>B. 21"<br>C. 24"<br>D. 28" | |
| 6. | Find the drop if the grade is 1/8" per foot and the run is 50 feet.<br><br>A. 6 1/4"<br>B. 6 1/2"<br>C. 6 3/4"<br>D. 7" | |

| | | |
|---|---|---|
| 7. | Find the percentage grade if the drop is 12 1/2 inches and the run is 100 feet.<br><br>A. 0.5%<br>B. 1%<br>C. 2%<br>D. 4% | |
| 8. | Find the percentage grade if the drop is 40 inches and the run is 160 feet.<br><br>A. 0.5%<br>B. 1%<br>C. 2%<br>D. 4% | |
| 9. | Find the drop if the percentage grade is 1% and the run is 80 feet.<br><br>A. 9 1/8"<br>B. 9 1/4"<br>C. 9 3/8"<br>D. 9 5/8" | |
| 10. | Find the drop if the percentage grade is 2% and the run is 50 feet.<br><br>A. 12"<br>B. 13"<br>C. 14"<br>D. 15" | |

## Water Pressure

As gravity pulls water down, pressure is created. The deeper the water, the greater the pressure at the bottom. Consider the case of a water tower, which is commonly used to supply pressurized water to communities. The tower's height will affect the amount of pressure that can be supplied.

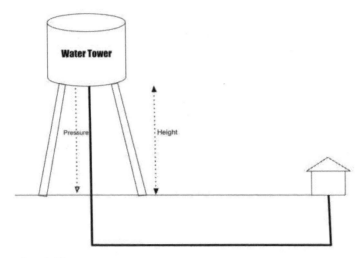

Figure 7-29

To understand how pressure is measured, we can start with something we can measure. If you had a container that was exactly one cubic foot, it would be one foot in length, width, and height. The base of the container would be one square foot. If we were to fill the container with water and put it on a scale, it would weigh 62.5 pounds. (Figure 7-30)

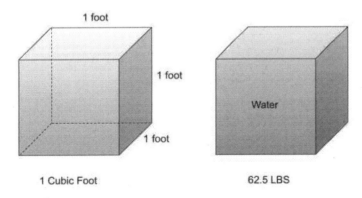

Figure 7-30

161

But we don't measure pressure in pounds per square foot, right? Pressure is generally measured in pounds per square inch (psi). To convert, we must divide the base area of the container by square inches. Since one square foot is the same as 144 square inches, we divide the 62.5 pounds that we measured by 144. The result is **0.434** pounds per square inch (psi). (Figure 7-31) This is another number that a plumber needs to have memorized! With 0.434, we can calculate the pressure of any column of water.

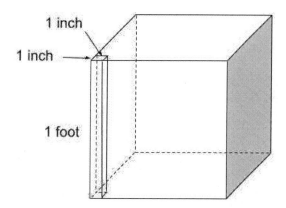

62.5 / 144 = 0.434 Pounds per Square Inch

Figure 7-31

**Example**: What is the pressure at the base of a water tower that is 85 feet high?

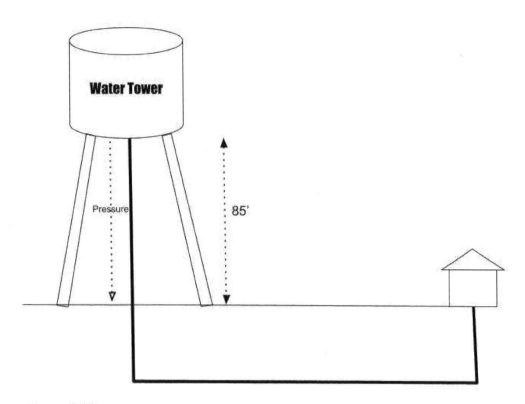

Figure 7-32

|  | Method | Example |
|---|---|---|
| Step 1: | Multiply the height in feet by 0.434. | 85 x 0.434 = **36.89 PSI** |

**Example**: What is the height of a water column in pipes if the pressure is 65 PSI?

|  | Method | Example |
|---|---|---|
| Step 1: | Divide the pressure by 0.434 to get the height in feet. | 65 ÷ 0.434 = **149.8 Feet** |

## Pressure - Practice Problems

| Number | Question | Answer |
|--------|----------|--------|
| 1. | What is the pressure at the base of a water tower that is 45 feet tall?<br><br>A. 18.4 psi<br>B. 19.5 psi<br>C. 20.2 psi<br>D. 21.1 psi | |
| 2. | What is the pressure at the base of a water tower that is 86 feet tall?<br><br>A. 36.1 psi<br>B. 36.5 psi<br>C. 36.9 psi<br>D. 37.2 psi | |
| 3. | What is the pressure if the water source is 160 feet above the point of delivery?<br><br>A. 68.5 psi<br>B. 69.3 psi<br>C. 70.1 psi<br>D. 71.3 psi | |
| 4. | How tall is a water tower if the pressure at the base is 43 psi?<br><br>A. 92 feet<br>B. 95 feet<br>C. 99 feet<br>D. 101 feet | |
| 5. | How tall is a water tower if the pressure at the base is 25 psi?<br><br>A. 55 feet<br>B. 58 feet<br>C. 60 feet<br>D. 63 feet | |

## Percentage Markup

Do you remember studying percentages? A percentage is a portion of something. 100% is the whole thing. To write a percentage, take the number in decimal form to the hundredth place (two zeros to the right of the decimal point), and then move the decimal point over to the right two decimal places, and write the percentage sign to the right side of the number.

| Decimal to Percentage | Method | Example |
|---|---|---|
| Step 1: | Write the number with decimal to the hundredths place. | ½ = .50 |
| Step 2: | Move the decimal point to the right two places and write a percent sign. | .50 = 50% |

To calculate a percentage, we use the decimal form, not the percentage. So, if we have a percentage, we must move the decimal point to places to the left to create a number we can calculate with.

| Percentage to Decimal | Method | Example |
|---|---|---|
| Step 1: | Move the decimal point to the left two places and remove the percent sign. . | 25% = 0.25 |

The markup is the amount of money charged to a customer and the cost of the materials. This is calculated by using a percentage. The percentage must be converted into a decimal and then added to the number 1 to create a price that has been marked up. This number is then multiplied by the cost of materials for the new price to the customer.

**Example:** A faucet costs $145 at the supplier. The plumber will sell the faucet with a markup of 30%. What is the new price for the faucet?

| Calculate Markup | Method | Example |
|---|---|---|
| Step 1: | Write the markup percent as a decimal. | 30% = 0.30 |
| Step 2: | Add the decimal to 1. | 1 + 0.30 = 1.30 |
| Step 3: | Multiply the number by the material cost to find the customer cost. | $145 x 1.30 = **$188.50** |

## Percentage Markup - Practice Problems

| Number | Question | Answer |
|--------|----------|--------|
| 1. | A fixture costs $167.00 at the supplier. The plumber will sell the fixture with a markup of 20%. What is the new price for the fixture?<br><br>A. $186.75<br>B. $193.50<br>C. $200.40<br>D. $225.35 | |
| 2. | A faucet costs $425.00 at the supplier. The plumber will sell the faucet with a markup of 15%. What is the new price for the faucet?<br><br>A. $488.75<br>B. $493.50<br>C. $500.60<br>D. $525.37 | |
| 3. | A water softener costs $765.00 at the supplier. The plumber will sell the water softener with a markup of 45%. What is the new price for the softener?<br><br>A. $1010.75<br>B. $1093.50<br>C. $1109.25<br>D. $1225.39 | |

## Math Review Test

Now that you have reviewed the important math concepts, it's time to test. Do your best without looking at examples or problems we have discussed. If you missed any questions, do not stress, they will serve as an indicator of what you ought to review again. This way, you can polish up the math concepts that need your attention. Good luck!

| Math Review Test | | |
|---|---|---|
| Number | Question | |
| 1 | Convert 7.58' to feet and fractional inches.<br><br>A. 7' 6 1/2"<br>B. 7' 7"<br>C. 7' 8"<br>D. 7' 9" | |
| 2 | How tall is a water tower if the pressure at the base is 55 psi?<br><br>A. 127 feet<br>B. 130 feet<br>C. 133 feet<br>D. 138 feet | |
| 3 | What is the pressure if the water source is 155 feet above the point of delivery?<br><br>A. 66.5 psi<br>B. 66.9 psi<br>C. 67.1 psi<br>D. 70.2 psi | |
| 4 | Calculate the diagonal for a rolling offset made with two 45 degree fittings which has a rise of 8 inches and an offset of 7 inches.<br><br>A. 12.54 inches<br>B. 13.24 inches<br>C. 14.52 inches<br>D. 15.03 inches | |
| 5 | Convert 8' 7 1/4" to decimal feet.<br><br>A. 8.55'<br>B. 8.60'<br>C. 8.65'<br>D. 8.70' | |

| | | |
|---|---|---|
| 6 | Calculate the volume of a cylindrical tank that has a diameter of 30' and a height of 20'.  (Use Pi = 3.14)<br><br>A. 1884 cubic feet<br>B. 942 cubic feet<br>C. 600 cubic feet<br>D. 14,130 cubic feet | |
| 7 | Calculate the diagonal for a pipe that offsets 36 inches using two 45 degree fittings.<br><br>A. 45.5 inches<br>B. 47.2 inches<br>C. 49.7 inches<br>D. 50.9 inches | |
| 8 | Convert 75 gallons into weight measurement in pounds.<br><br>A. 625 pounds<br>B. 630 pounds<br>C. 635 pounds<br>D. 640 pounds | |
| 9 | A toilet costs $257.00 at the supplier. The plumber will sell the toilet with a markup of 25%. What is the new price for the toilet?<br><br>A. $295.75<br>B. $321.25<br>C. $343.95<br>D. $355.90 | |
| 10 | Find the drop if the grade is 1/8" per foot and the run is 100 feet.<br><br>A. 12 1/4"<br>B. 12 1/2"<br>C. 12 3/4"<br>D. 13" | |

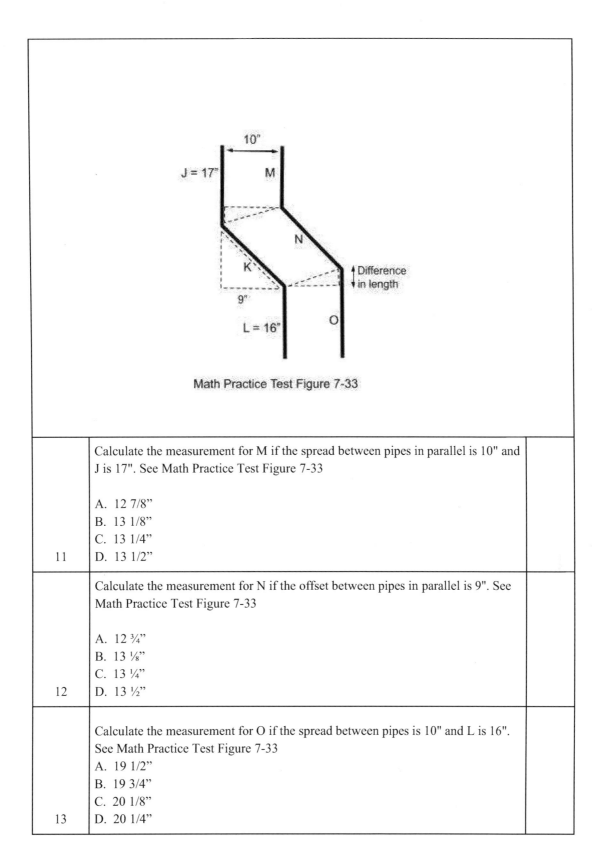

Math Practice Test Figure 7-33

| | |
|---|---|
| | Calculate the measurement for M if the spread between pipes in parallel is 10" and J is 17". See Math Practice Test Figure 7-33 |
| | |
| | A. 12 7/8" |
| | B. 13 1/8" |
| | C. 13 1/4" |
| 11 | D. 13 1/2" |
| | Calculate the measurement for N if the offset between pipes in parallel is 9". See Math Practice Test Figure 7-33 |
| | |
| | A. 12 ¾" |
| | B. 13 ⅛" |
| | C. 13 ¼" |
| 12 | D. 13 ½" |
| | Calculate the measurement for O if the spread between pipes is 10" and L is 16". See Math Practice Test Figure 7-33 |
| | A. 19 1/2" |
| | B. 19 3/4" |
| | C. 20 1/8" |
| 13 | D. 20 1/4" |

169

| | | |
|---|---|---|
| 14 | Find the drop if the grade is 1/4" per foot and the run is 30 feet.<br><br>A. 7 1/4"<br>B. 7 1/2"<br>C. 7 3/4"<br>D. 8" | |
| 15 | Find the percentage grade if the drop is 5 inches and the run is 40 feet.<br><br>A. 0.5%<br>B. 1%<br>C. 2%<br>D. 4% | |
| 16 | Convert 2.375" to fractional inches.<br><br>A. 2 1/4"<br>B. 2 5/16"<br>C. 2 3/8"<br>D. 2 7/16" | |
| 17 | Convert 8 3/16" to decimal inches.<br><br>A. 8.125"<br>B. 8.143"<br>C. 8.165"<br>D. 8.187" | |
| 18 | Calculate the diagonal for a pipe that offsets 40 inches using two 45 degree fittings.<br><br>A. 52.6 inches<br>B. 56.5 inches<br>C. 58.1 inches<br>D. 60.8 inches | |
| 19 | Convert 39' 9 7/8" to decimal feet.<br><br>A. 39.65'<br>B. 39.77'<br>C. 39.82'<br>D. 39.90' | |

| | | |
|---|---|---|
| 20 | Find the drop if the percentage grade is 1% and the run is 40 feet.<br><br>A. 4 3/8"<br>B. 4 1/2"<br>C. 4 3/4"<br>D. 4 7/8" | |
| 21 | Find the area of a tank base that has a diameter of 18 feet. (Use Pi = 3.14)<br><br>A. 180 square feet<br>B. 202 square feet<br>C. 224 square feet<br>D. 254 square feet | |
| 22 | Find the grade of a pipe if the drop is 7 1/4" and the run is 58 feet.<br><br>A. 1/16" per foot<br>B. 1/8" per foot<br>C. 1/4" per foot<br>D. 1/2" per foot | |
| 23 | Convert 7' 5 1/8" to decimal feet.<br><br>A. 7.37'<br>B. 7.43'<br>C. 7.46'<br>D. 7.49' | |
| 24 | Convert 9 1/8" to decimal inches.<br><br>A. 9.110"<br>B. 9.115"<br>C. 9.120"<br>D. 9.125" | |
| 25 | A faucet costs $675.00 at the supplier. The plumber will sell the faucet with a markup of 25%. What is the new price for the faucet?<br><br>A. $786.75<br>B. $793.50<br>C. $810.40<br>D. $843.75 | |

| | | |
|---|---|---|
| 26 | Convert 3.687" to fractional inches.<br><br>A. 3 5/8"<br>B. 3 11/16"<br>C. 3 3/4"<br>D. 3 13/16" | |
| 27 | Convert 10 cubic feet into gallons.<br><br>A. 75 gallons<br>B. 85 gallons<br>C. 95 gallons<br>D. 100 gallons | |
| 28 | Convert 13.91' to feet and fractional inches.<br><br>A. 13' 9"<br>B. 13' 10"<br>C. 13' 11"<br>D. 13' 11 1/2" | |

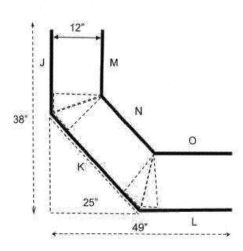

Math Practice Test Figure 7-34

| | | |
|---|---|---|
| 29 | Calculate the measurement for a special case 90 degree offset using 45 degree elbows for N if the spread between pipes is 12". See Math Practice Test Figure 7-34<br><br>A. 24 7/8"<br>B. 25 1/8"<br>C. 25 3/16"<br>D. 25 7/16" | |

| | | |
|---|---|---|
| 30 | Calculate the measurement for a special case 90 degree offset using 45 degree elbows for O if the spread between pipes is 12". See Math Practice Test Figure 7-34<br><br>A. 18 7/8"<br>B. 18 15/16"<br>C. 19 1/16"<br>D. 19 3/16" | |
| 31 | Calculate the measurement for a special case 90 degree offset using 45 degree elbows for M if the spread between pipes is 12". See Math Practice Test Figure 7-34<br><br>A. 8 1/16"<br>B. 8 1/4"<br>C. 8 3/8"<br>D. 8 1/2" | |
| 32 | Convert 41,472 cubic inches into cubic feet.<br><br>A. 24 cubic feet<br>B. 25 cubic feet<br>C. 26 cubic feet<br>D. 27 cubic feet | |
| 33 | Convert 10 3/4" to decimal inches.<br><br>A. 10.65"<br>B. 10.75"<br>C. 10.80"<br>D. 10.85" | |
| 34 | Calculate the diagonal for a rolling offset made with two 45 degree fittings which has a rise of 5 inches and an offset of 4 inches.<br><br>A. 8.40 inches<br>B. 8.75 inches<br>C. 9.05 inches<br>D. 9.25 inches | |
| 35 | Find the volume of a tub that is 32" wide, 72" long and 17" deep on inside dimensions.<br><br>A. 544 cubic inches<br>B. 2304 cubic inches<br>C. 1224 cubic inches<br>D. 39,168 cubic inches | |

| | | |
|---|---|---|
| 36 | Convert 20,736 cubic inches into cubic feet.<br><br>A. 10 cubic feet<br>B. 11 cubic feet<br>C. 12 cubic feet<br>D. 14 cubic feet | |
| 37 | Find the grade of a pipe if the drop is 7" and the run is 56 feet.<br><br>A. 1/16" per foot<br>B. 1/8" per foot<br>C. 1/4" per foot<br>D. 1/2" per foot | |
| 38 | Convert 270 gallons to cubic feet.<br><br>A. 30 cubic feet<br>B. 32 cubic feet<br>C. 36 cubic feet<br>D. 42 cubic feet | |
| 39 | What is the pressure at the base of a water tower that is 115 feet tall?<br><br>A. 49.9 psi<br>B. 50.6 psi<br>C. 51.2 psi<br>D. 52.2 psi | |
| 40 | Find the area of a room that is 14' in width and 18' in length.<br><br>A. 180 square feet<br>B. 192 square feet<br>C. 252 square feet<br>D. 274 square feet | |

## Conversion Practice Problems

| Number | Answer |
| --- | --- |
| 1 | B |
| 2 | C |
| 3 | C |
| 4 | B |
| 5 | B |
| 6 | C |
| 7 | A |
| 8 | C |
| 9 | B |
| 10 | D |
| 11 | C |
| 12 | A |
| 13 | C |
| 14 | D |
| 15 | C |
| 16 | D |

## Area Practice Problems

| Number | Answer |
| --- | --- |
| 1 | B |
| 2 | D |
| 3 | C |
| 4 | A |
| 5 | B |
| 6 | C |

## Volume Practice Problems

| Number | Answer |
|--------|--------|
| 1 | B |
| 2 | A |
| 3 | B |
| 4 | B |

## Converting Cubic Inches to Cubic Feet Practice Problems

| Number | Answer |
|--------|--------|
| 1 | C |
| 2 | B |
| 3 | C |
| 4 | A |

## Converting Cubic Feet into Gallons Practice Problems

| Number | Answer |
|--------|--------|
| 1 | C |
| 2 | D |
| 3 | B |
| 4 | A |

## Gallon to Pounds Practice Problems

| Number | Answer |
|--------|--------|
| 1 | C |
| 2 | C |
| 3 | D |

## Offset Practice Problems

| Number | Answer |
|--------|--------|
| 1 | C |
| 2 | D |
| 3 | D |
| 4 | B |

## Rolling Offset Practice Problems

| Number | Answer |
|--------|--------|
| 1 | B |
| 2 | D |
| 3 | A |
| 4 | A |

## 45 Offsets in Parallel Practice Problems

| Number | Answer |
|--------|--------|
| 1 | C |
| 2 | A |
| 3 | D |

## Special Case 45 Offsets Practice Problems

| Number | Answer |
|--------|--------|
| 1 | B |
| 2 | C |
| 3 | B |

## Grade Practice Problems

| Number | Answer |
|--------|--------|
| 1 | C |
| 2 | D |
| 3 | A |
| 4 | B |
| 5 | A |
| 6 | A |
| 7 | B |
| 8 | C |
| 9 | D |
| 10 | A |

## Pressure Practice Problems

| Number | Answer |
|--------|--------|
| 1 | B |
| 2 | D |
| 3 | B |
| 4 | C |
| 5 | B |

| Markup Practice Questions | |
|---|---|
| Number | Answer |
| 1 | C |
| 2 | A |
| 3 | C |

| Math Review Test | |
|---|---|
| Number | Answer |
| 1 | B |
| 2 | A |
| 3 | C |
| 4 | D |
| 5 | B |
| 6 | D |
| 7 | D |
| 8 | A |
| 9 | B |
| 10 | B |
| 11 | A |
| 12 | A |
| 13 | C |
| 14 | B |
| 15 | B |
| 16 | C |
| 17 | D |
| 18 | B |
| 19 | C |
| 20 | D |

| | |
|---|---|
| 21 | D |
| 22 | B |
| 23 | B |
| 24 | D |
| 25 | D |
| 26 | B |
| 27 | A |
| 28 | C |
| 29 | D |
| 30 | C |
| 31 | A |
| 32 | A |
| 33 | B |
| 34 | C |
| 35 | D |
| 36 | C |
| 37 | B |
| 38 | C |
| 39 | A |
| 40 | C |

Made in United States
Orlando, FL
13 November 2024

53852767R00100